CGP — revision that's right up your alloy...

Chemistry exams can seem daunting, but they're a whole lot less scary when you know what to expect. That's where this brilliant CGP book comes in...

It's full to the brim with exam-style questions for Edexcel's Grade 9-1 International GCSE Chemistry* course — plus two complete practice exam papers to make sure you're 100% ready for the real thing.

Better yet, we've included step-by-step answers at the back of the book — perfect for working out how to pick up every last mark!

* It's great for the Chemistry parts of the Edexcel International GCSE Science Double Award too.

CGP — still the best! ☺

Our sole aim here at CGP is to produce the highest quality books — carefully written, immaculately presented and dangerously close to being funny.

Then we work our socks off to get them out to you — at the cheapest possible prices.

Contents

✓ Use the tick boxes to check off the topics you've completed.

Published by CGP

Editors:
Alex Billings, Robin Flello, Rachel Kordan and Sarah Pattison

Contributor:
Paddy Gannon

With thanks to Katherine Faudemer, Ciara McGlade, Jamie Sinclair and Hayley Thompson for the proofreading.

With thanks to Ana Pungartnik for the copyright research.

ISBN: 978 1 78294 686 1

Clipart from Corel®
Printed by Elanders Ltd, Newcastle upon Tyne

Based on the classic CGP style created by Richard Parsons.

2

How To Use This Book

- Hold the book <u>upright</u>, approximately <u>50 cm</u> from your face, ensuring that the text looks like <u>this</u>, not s̄ı̄ɥ̄ʇ̄. Alternatively, place the book on a <u>horizontal</u> surface (e.g. a table or desk) and sit adjacent to the book, at a distance which doesn't make the text too small to read.
- In case of emergency, press the two halves of the book together <u>firmly</u> in order to close.
- Before attempting to use this book, familiarise yourself with the following <u>safety information</u>:

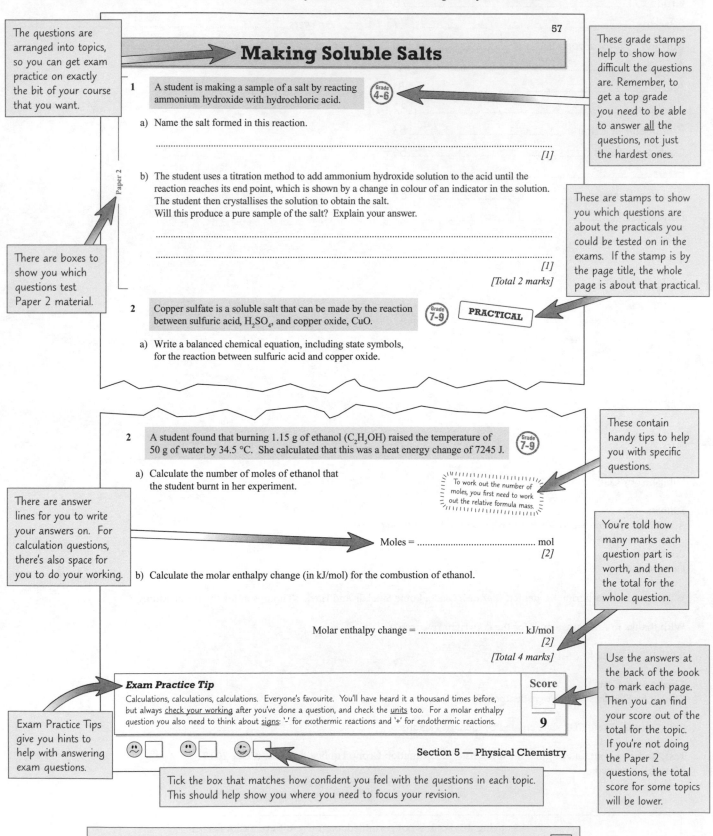

The questions are arranged into topics, so you can get exam practice on exactly the bit of your course that you want.

These grade stamps help to show how difficult the questions are. Remember, to get a top grade you need to be able to answer <u>all</u> the questions, not just the hardest ones.

There are boxes to show you which questions test Paper 2 material.

These are stamps to show you which questions are about the practicals you could be tested on in the exams. If the stamp is by the page title, the whole page is about that practical.

57

Making Soluble Salts

Paper 2

1 A student is making a sample of a salt by reacting ammonium hydroxide with hydrochloric acid. Grade 4-6

a) Name the salt formed in this reaction.

....
[1]

b) The student uses a titration method to add ammonium hydroxide solution to the acid until the reaction reaches its end point, which is shown by a change in colour of an indicator in the solution. The student then crystallises the solution to obtain the salt.
Will this produce a pure sample of the salt? Explain your answer.

....

....
[1]
[Total 2 marks]

2 Copper sulfate is a soluble salt that can be made by the reaction between sulfuric acid, H_2SO_4, and copper oxide, CuO. Grade 7-9 PRACTICAL

a) Write a balanced chemical equation, including state symbols, for the reaction between sulfuric acid and copper oxide.

These contain handy tips to help you with specific questions.

2 A student found that burning 1.15 g of ethanol (C_2H_5OH) raised the temperature of 50 g of water by 34.5 °C. She calculated that this was a heat energy change of 7245 J. Grade 7-9

a) Calculate the number of moles of ethanol that the student burnt in her experiment.

To work out the number of moles, you first need to work out the relative formula mass.

There are answer lines for you to write your answers on. For calculation questions, there's also space for you to do your working.

Moles = ... mol
[2]

You're told how many marks each question part is worth, and then the total for the whole question.

b) Calculate the molar enthalpy change (in kJ/mol) for the combustion of ethanol.

Molar enthalpy change = ... kJ/mol
[2]
[Total 4 marks]

Use the answers at the back of the book to mark each page. Then you can find your score out of the total for the topic. If you're not doing the Paper 2 questions, the total score for some topics will be lower.

Exam Practice Tip
Calculations, calculations, calculations. Everyone's favourite. You'll have heard it a thousand times before, but always <u>check your working</u> after you've done a question, and check the <u>units</u> too. For a molar enthalpy question you also need to think about <u>signs</u>: '–' for exothermic reactions and '+' for endothermic reactions.

Score
☐
9

Exam Practice Tips give you hints to help with answering exam questions.

😞 ☐   😐 ☐   🙂 ☐

Section 5 — Physical Chemistry

Tick the box that matches how confident you feel with the questions in each topic. This should help show you where you need to focus your revision.

Some questions are multiple choice. You'll need to answer them by putting a cross in a box, like this: ☒

How To Use This Book

Exam Tips

Before you get cracking on some exam practice, here's some handy information and some tips to help you in the exams.

Edexcel International GCSE Exam Stuff

1) For the Edexcel International GCSE in Chemistry, you'll sit two exam papers at the end of your course. ➡

2) Some material in the specification will only be tested in Paper 2. The questions that cover Paper 2 material in this book are marked with a Paper 2 box.

Paper	Time	No. of marks
1	2 hours	110
2	1 hr 15 mins	70

You Need to Understand the Command Words

Command words are the words in a question that tell you what to do.
If you don't know what they mean, you might not be able to answer the questions properly.

Describe — This means you need to recall facts or write about what something is like.

Explain — You have to give reasons for something or say why or how something happens.

State — This means the same thing as 'Name...' or 'Give...'.
You usually just have to give a short definition or an example of something.

Suggest — You need to use your knowledge to work out the answer. It'll often be something you haven't been taught, but you should be able to use what you know to figure it out.

Calculate — This means you'll have to use numbers from the question to work something out. You'll probably have to get your calculator out.

Seven Golden Rules for your Exam

1) **Always, always, always make sure you read the question properly.**
For example, if the question asks you to give your answer in cm^3, don't give it in dm^3.

2) **Look at the number of marks a question is worth.**
The number of marks gives you a pretty good clue of how much to write. So if a question is worth four marks, make sure you write four decent points. And there's no point writing an essay for a question that's only worth one mark — it's just a waste of your time.

3) **Write your answers as clearly as you can.**
If the examiner can't read your answer you won't get any marks, even if it's right.

4) **Use specialist vocabulary.**
You know the words I mean — the sciencey ones, like enthalpy change and polymerisation. Examiners love them.

5) **Show each step in your calculations.**
You're less likely to make a mistake if you write things out in steps. And even if your final answer's wrong, you'll probably pick up some marks if the examiner can see that your method is right. You also need to make sure you're working in the right units — check before you put any numbers in your calculator.

6) **Pay attention to the time.**
Don't spend ages staring at the question paper. If you're totally, hopelessly stuck on a question, just leave it and move on to the next one. You can always go back to it at the end if you've got enough time.

> Obeying these Golden Rules will help you get as many marks as you can in the exams — but they're no use if you haven't learnt the stuff in the first place. So make sure you revise well and do as many practice questions as you can.

7) **Be prepared and try not to panic.**
Exam day can give anyone a case of the jitters. So make sure you've got everything you need for the exam (pen, spare pen, pencil, ruler, calculator) ready the night before. Eat a good breakfast. And try to relax...

Section 1 — Particles and Mixtures

States of Matter

1 Substances can exist in three states of matter: solid, liquid or gas. *(Grade 3-4)*

a) In which of these three states of matter are the forces of attraction between the particles **strongest**?

....

[1]

b) Name the state of matter illustrated in the diagram below.

....

[1]

c) Describe the movement of particles in a gas.

....

[1]

[Total 3 marks]

2 The diagram shows a substance changing between solid, liquid and gas states. *(Grade 4-6)*

a) Give the letter of the arrow that represents **subliming**.

....

[1]

b) Give the name of the process represented by arrow A. ....

[1]

c) Describe what happens to the particles in a solid when it is heated to the point of melting.

....

....

....

....

[4]

[Total 6 marks]

Score:

9

Movement of Particles

1   A student placed a small amount of potassium manganate(VII) in a beaker of water. The potassium manganate(VII) completely dissolved, turning the water nearby purple. Eventually all the water in the beaker was purple.

(Grade 3-4)

a) Give the name of the process which made the colour spread through the beaker.

....
                                                                                                    [1]

b) The student then added more water to the beaker. Which sentence correctly explains what happened to the colour of the water?

☐ **A** The colour was unchanged as the amount of potassium manganate(VII) stayed the same.

☐ **B** The colour was unchanged as water particles don't react with potassium manganate(VII).

☐ **C** The water got less purple as some of the potassium manganate(VII) particles reacted.

☐ **D** The water got less purple as the potassium manganate(VII) particles spread further apart.
                                                                                                    [1]

c) The result of the student's next experiment is shown below. A white ring of ammonium chloride has formed on the glass tube at the point where the hydrogen chloride gas met the ammonia gas.

sealed glass tube   ring of ammonium chloride

source of ammonia gas   source of hydrogen chloride gas

Which sentence correctly explains why the ring formed closer to the source of hydrogen chloride than the source of ammonia?

☐ **A** The air was warmer near the source of the hydrogen chloride, so it evaporated more quickly.

☐ **B** The particles of ammonia are smaller and lighter, so they diffused more quickly.

☐ **C** The particles of ammonia were diluted by the air in the tube.

☐ **D** The particles of hydrogen chloride gas vibrated about a fixed position.
                                                                                                    [1]
                                                                                        [Total 3 marks]

2   In the experiment shown in the diagram, a gas jar full of brown bromine gas is separated from a gas jar full of air by a glass plate.

(Grade 4-6)

The glass plate is then removed.
Describe and explain the appearance of the gas jars after an hour.

bromine

glass plate

air

....

....

....
                                                                                                    [2]
                                                                                        [Total 2 marks]

Score: ☐

5

☹ ☐   ☺ ☐   ☺ ☐

Solubility

1 A student is preparing a solution of sodium chloride in a beaker of water. (Grade 4-6)

a) Define the term '**solution**'.

....

....

[2]

b) The student keeps adding sodium chloride to the beaker and stirring the solution.
Eventually, the sodium chloride starts to settle at the bottom of the beaker. Explain why.

....

....

[1]

[Total 3 marks]

2 The table below shows the solubility of a substance in water at different temperatures. (Grade 6-7)

Temperature / °C	0	10	20	30	40
Solubility / g per 100 g of water	12.0	14.0	16.5	19.5	23

a) Draw a graph to show this data. Draw a curved line of best fit through the points on the graph.

[4]

b) Use the graph you plotted in part a) to determine the solubility of the substance at 25 °C.

....

[1]

[Total 5 marks]

Score:

8

Section 1 — Particles and Mixtures

Investigating Solubility

PRACTICAL

1 A student is carrying out an experiment to find the solubility of a substance at 30 °C. **Grade 6-7**

a) The student starts by heating a saturated solution to 30 °C. Which of the following pieces of apparatus would be most suitable for evenly heating the solution?

☐ **A** Desiccator   ☐ **C** Evaporating dish

☐ **B** Water bath   ☐ **D** Bunsen burner

[1]

b) The student then heats a known mass of the saturated solution until all the water has evaporated.

Suggest a hazard that could be associated with this experiment, and give **one** way that the student could reduce the risk involved with this hazard.

....

....

[2]

c) The student's results are shown in the table.

Mass of solid obtained / g	12.2
Mass of water removed / g	32.8

Calculate the solubility of potassium chloride at 30 °C.
Give your answer to three significant figures.

solubility = ... g per 100 g of water

[2]

d) Suggest one way that the student could improve the reliability of the experiment.

....

[1]

e) State the dependent variable in the experiment.

....

[1]

[Total 7 marks]

Exam Practice Tip

Around 20% of the marks in the exam could come from questions testing your knowledge of experimental skills, so make sure you're comfortable with what terms like 'reliability' mean in the context of chemistry. You might also be asked do some calculations with experimental data, or how an experiment could be improved.

Score

☐

7

 ☐   ☐   ☐

Section 1 — Particles and Mixtures

Atoms

1 Atoms are made up of protons, neutrons and electrons.

a) Complete the table.

Particle	Relative mass	Charge
Proton	....	+1
Neutron	1	....
Electron	....	−1

[3]

b) State the name for a group of atoms held together by covalent bonds. ....

[1]

[Total 4 marks]

2 A manganese atom can be represented by the nuclear symbol $^{55}_{25}$Mn.

a) State the mass number and atomic number of $^{55}_{25}$Mn.

mass number: ....

atomic number: ....

[2]

b) How many protons, neutrons and electrons does an atom of $^{55}_{25}$Mn have?

protons: ....   neutrons: ....   electrons: ....

[3]

[Total 5 marks]

3 The diagram below shows part of the structure of a neutral atom with a mass number of 11.

a) What is the name for the part of the atom below that is shaded grey? ....

[1]

b) The diagram is incomplete.
Electrons are shown on the diagram using ×.
Complete the diagram using:
   ● to represent protons,
   ■ to represent neutrons.

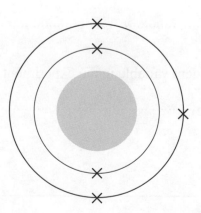

[2]

[Total 3 marks]

Score:
12

Isotopes and Relative Atomic Mass

1 Two of the most common isotopes of chlorine are chlorine-35 (^{35}Cl) and chlorine-37 (^{37}Cl). **Grade 4-6**

a) State what is meant by the term **isotope**.

....

....
[2]

b) Complete the following table to show the mass number and the numbers of protons and neutrons in each of these chlorine isotopes.

Isotope	Mass number	Number of protons	Number of neutrons
^{35}Cl	35	17	
^{37}Cl			

[2]

[Total 4 marks]

2 The relative atomic mass of every element can be found in the periodic table. **Grade 6-7**

a) Give the definition of the **relative atomic mass** of an element.

....

....
[2]

b) Suggest why some elements have relative atomic masses that are not whole numbers.

....

....
[1]

[Total 3 marks]

3 Gallium can exist as two stable isotopes: Ga-69 and Ga-71. **Grade 7-9**

60.1% of gallium atoms are Ga-69 atoms, and the rest are Ga-71 atoms.
Calculate the relative atomic mass of gallium.

relative atomic mass = ...
[Total 3 marks]

Exam Practice Tip

Definitions can be tricky to remember but it's worth learning them because they are a good way of picking up easy marks. Just keep writing them down until they are stuck in your head. The definitions of isotopes and relative atomic mass are a good place to start. So what are you waiting for — get scribbling....

Score

[ ]

10

Section 1 — Particles and Mixtures

Elements, Compounds and Mixtures

1 Many everyday substances, such as copper, are elements.
Other substances, such as table salt, are compounds.

(Grade 3-4)

Briefly describe the difference between an **element** and a **compound**.

....

....

[Total 2 marks]

2 Copper can be made extremely pure. The melting points of two samples
of copper were measured. Sample **A** had a melting point of 1085 °C
and sample **B** melted over the range 900 – 940 °C.

(Grade 4-6)

Suggest which of the samples, **A** or **B**, was the **most pure**. Explain your answer.

....

....

....

[Total 2 marks]

3 The photograph shows the NASA Space Shuttle soon after being launched.

(Grade 4-6)

The large central tank contains liquid oxygen and liquid hydrogen.
In the shuttle's thrusters, oxygen reacts with hydrogen to produce water vapour.

State whether each of the substances below is an element, compound or mixture.
Explain your answer in each case.

Water vapour ....

....

Liquid oxygen ....

....

[Total 4 marks]

Score:

8

Separating Mixtures

1   Different groups of seaweed contain different types of a pigment called chlorophyll.

The table below shows which types of chlorophyll each group of seaweed contains.

Group of seaweed	Type of chlorophyll		
	a	b	c
Red	✓		
Brown	✓		✓
Green	✓	✓	

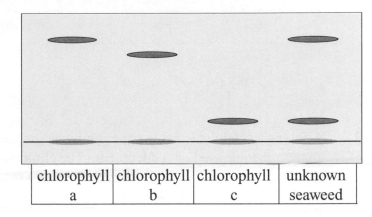

| chlorophyll a | chlorophyll b | chlorophyll c | unknown seaweed |

Use the chromatogram on the right to identify which group the unknown seaweed belongs to.

....

[Total 1 mark]

2   The diagram below shows a set of equipment you could use for separating a mixture in the lab.

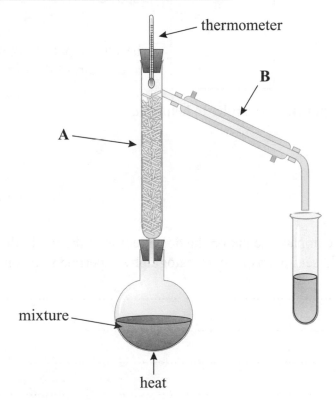

a)   Name the pieces of equipment labelled **A** and **B**.

A ....

B ....

[2]

b) Explain how fractional distillation works to separate a mixture of liquids.

....

....

....

....

....

[4]

[Total 6 marks]

3 A forensic scientist is using paper chromatography to analyse the ink used on a document. The chromatogram she produced is shown in the diagram below.

Grade 6-7

PRACTICAL

furthest point reached by the solvent

spot **A**

spot **B**

spot **C**

baseline (spot of ink was put on this line at the start of the experiment)

a) Calculate the R_f value of spot **B**. Use a ruler to help you.

R_f = ...

[3]

b) i) The scientist wants to compare the ink on the document with the ink in three different printers. Describe how she could set up a paper chromatography experiment to compare the inks.

....

....

....

....

[3]

ii) Explain how her results could be used to identify the printer that produced the document.

....

....

[1]

[Total 7 marks]

4 Sodium chloride dissolves in water, but not in ethanol.
Sodium chloride has a melting point of 801 °C and a boiling point of 1413 °C.
Ethanol has a melting point of −114 °C and a boiling point of 78 °C.

a) Suggest a purification method which would separate a mixture of sodium chloride and ethanol, but **not** a mixture of sodium chloride and water. Explain your answer.

....

....

....

....

[3]

b) Suggest a purification method which would separate a mixture of sodium chloride and water and would **also** separate a mixture of sodium chloride and ethanol. Explain your answer.

....

....

....

[2]

[Total 5 marks]

5 The table below lists the boiling points of three compounds.

Name	Formula	Boiling point / °C
cyclopentane	C_5H_{10}	49
ethanol	C_2H_6O	78
ethyl ethanoate	$C_4H_8O_2$	77

Suggest why a mixture of ethanol and ethyl ethanoate might be more difficult to separate than a mixture of ethanol and cyclopentane.

....

....

....

....

....

[Total 2 marks]

Score: ⬜

21

Section 1 — Particles and Mixtures

Section 2 — The Periodic Table and Bonding

The Periodic Table

1 The periodic table contains all the elements arranged in order. *(Grade 3-4)*

a) How are the elements arranged in the periodic table?

☐ **A** By atomic number   ☐ **C** By mass number

☐ **B** By electron number   ☐ **D** By neutron number

[1]

b) What is the name given to the rows in the periodic table? ....

[1]

[Total 2 marks]

2 The diagram shows some of the elements in the periodic table. *(Grade 6-7)*

Group 1	Group 2											Group 3	Group 4	Group 5	Group 6	Group 7	Group 0
	Be											B	C	N	O	F	
	Mg											Al			S		
K	Ca																Kr

a) Write the symbol of an element shown in the diagram that:

i) has seven outer electrons ....

[1]

ii) has a full outer electron shell ....

[1]

iii) has one outer electron ....

[1]

b) Give the name of an element shown on the diagram that has similar chemical properties
to magnesium. Explain your answer in terms of electronic configuration.

....

....

[2]

[Total 5 marks]

Exam Practice Tip

You won't be expected to memorise the periodic table for the exam — you'll always be given a copy of it.
It's dead handy. Amongst other things, you can use it to work out the number of electrons in an atom.
Remember, the number of electrons in an atom's outer shell is the same as its group number.

Score

☐

7

Electron Shells

1 The atomic number of neon is 10. *(Grade 4-6)*

How many electrons does neon have in its **outer shell**?

☐ **A** 2 ☐ **B** 6 ☐ **C** 8 ☐ **D** 10

[Total 1 mark]

2 The atomic number of sulfur is 16. *(Grade 6-7)*

a) Write down the electronic structure of sulfur.

....

[1]

b) Draw a diagram to show how the electrons are arranged in a single sulfur atom.

[1]

[Total 2 marks]

3 Magnesium is found in group 2 and period 3 of the periodic table. *(Grade 6-7)*

a) Explain how you could use this information to deduce the electronic structure of magnesium.

....

....

....

....

....

[3]

b) Give the electronic structure of magnesium.

....

[1]

[Total 4 marks]

Score: ☐

7

 ☐ ☐ ☐

More on the Periodic Table

1 Elements can be classified as metals or non-metals.

Grade 4-6

Use the periodic table on the inside back cover to help you answer questions a and b.

a) Which of these elements is a metal?

☐ **A** carbon ☐ **B** barium ☐ **C** chlorine ☐ **D** selenium

[1]

b) Elements can be classified as metals or non-metals based on the acid-base nature of their oxide. Which of these oxides will dissolve to form a solution with a pH of less than 7?

☐ **A** calcium oxide ☐ **B** iron oxide ☐ **C** copper oxide ☐ **D** sulfur dioxide

[1]

c) The diagram below shows the position of the element bismuth in the periodic table.

line **A** →

Bi

Element **X** is found in the same group of the periodic table as bismuth. Element **X** does not conduct electricity. Predict whether element **X** will be found to the left or the right of line **A** in the diagram. Explain your answer.

....

....

[2]

[Total 4 marks]

2 Some light bulbs contain a thin metal filament. If these bulbs were filled with air, oxygen would react with the filament causing it to burn away. To avoid this, the light bulbs are filled with argon.

Grade 6-7

Explain why argon is suitable for this use.

....

....

....

....

[Total 2 marks]

Score: ☐

6

Ionic Bonding

1 Which diagram shows the formation of an oxide ion from an oxygen atom? (Grade 3-4)

☐ A

☐ C

☐ B

☐ D

[Total 1 mark]

2 Potassium chloride (KCl) is an ionic compound containing potassium ions bonded to chloride ions. (Grade 4-6)

a) Describe the bonding between the potassium ions and chloride ions in potassium chloride.

....

....

[2]

b) i) Potassium is in Group 1. Deduce the formula of a potassium ion. ....

[1]

ii) Chlorine is in Group 7. Deduce the formula of a chloride ion. ....

[1]

[Total 4 marks]

3 Sodium atoms can react to form sodium ions. (Grade 6-7)

a) Sulfur and chlorine both react with sodium to form ionic compounds.
Explain how you can use the positions of sulfur and chlorine in the periodic table
to predict the number of electrons they will gain when they form ions.

....

....

....

[2]

b) Sodium nitrate ($NaNO_3$) is an ionic compound containing sodium ions bonded with nitrate ions.
Explain why nitrate ions cannot form ionic compounds with bromide ions.

....

....

[2]

[Total 4 marks]

Score: ☐

9

Section 2 — The Periodic Table and Bonding

Ionic Compounds

1   The diagram below shows the formation of the ionic compound lithium chloride from its elements, but it is incomplete.

a) Complete the diagram below by drawing an arrow to show the transfer of the electron, adding the charges of the ions and completing the chloride ion to show the electrons in its outer shell.

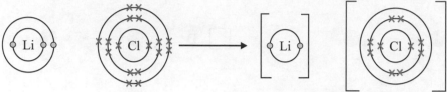

[3]

b) State the overall charge of lithium chloride.

....
[1]
[Total 4 marks]

2   This question is about the structure and properties of ionic compounds. _Grade 4-6_

a) Which of the following properties is **not** typical for an ionic compound?

☐ **A** high boiling point

☐ **B** conduct electricity in the liquid state

☐ **C** soluble in water

☐ **D** conduct electricity in the solid state

[1]

b) Name the type of structure that ionic compounds have.

....
[1]
[Total 2 marks]

3   The diagram below shows the ions in an ionic compound. All of the electrons are shown. _Grade 6-7_

Identify the positive and negative ions in this compound.

Positive ....

Negative ....

> From the dots and the crosses, you can see how many electrons each ion has gained or lost. You can use the periodic table to work out what atom it was to start with.

[Total 2 marks]

Section 2 — The Periodic Table and Bonding

4 A student reacts magnesium nitrate with potassium hydroxide. **Grade 6-7**
The products of the reaction are magnesium hydroxide and potassium nitrate.

Write the chemical formulae of magnesium hydroxide and potassium nitrate.

magnesium hydroxide ....

potassium nitrate ....

[Total 2 marks]

5 Sodium oxide, Na_2O, is an ionic compound. **Grade 6-7**

Draw a dot and cross diagram to show the bonding in sodium oxide.
You should include the charges on the ions in your diagram.

[Total 4 marks]

6 Sodium chloride is an ionic compound. **Grade 6-7**

a) Describe the structure of a crystal of sodium chloride. You should state:
- What particles are present in the crystal.
- How these particles are arranged.
- What holds the particles together.

....

....

....

....

....

[4]

b) Explain why sodium chloride has a high melting point.

....

....

[2]

[Total 6 marks]

Exam Practice Tip

Don't panic if you're asked about an ionic compound that you haven't met before. Think about what you <u>do</u> know about ionic compounds, and read the question carefully to make sure you've picked up on any extra info you've been given. Oh, and check your answer afterwards to make sure you've actually answered the question...

Score

20

Covalent Bonding

1 The bonding in phosphorus trichloride (PCl_3) is shown in the dot and cross diagram. Only the outer electrons are shown.

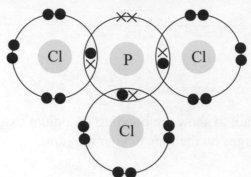

a) State how many electrons there are in the outer shell of each atom in PCl_3 ....

[1]

b) State how many shared pairs of electrons there are in a molecule of PCl_3 ....

[1]

c) State how many double covalent bonds there are in a molecule of PCl_3 ....

[1]

[Total 3 marks]

2 Dot and cross diagrams can be used to show the position of electrons in covalent molecules.

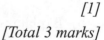

Complete the dot and cross diagrams for the molecules below. Only show the outer electrons.

a) hydrogen chloride, HCl   b) oxygen, O_2 c) ammonia, NH_3

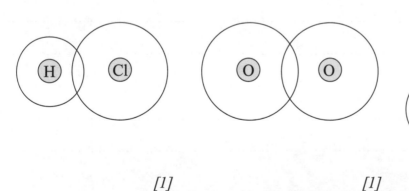

[1]   *[1]*   *[1]*

[Total 3 marks]

3 Silicon has the electronic structure 2.8.4.

Use this information to predict the maximum number of covalent bonds one atom of silicon can form in a simple molecule. Explain your answer.

....

....

....

[Total 2 marks]

Section 2 — The Periodic Table and Bonding

4 Hydrocarbon gases such as ethane (C_2H_6) are useful chemicals. **Grade 6-7**

a) Draw a dot and cross diagram of ethane. Only show the outer electrons of each atom.

[2]

b) Explain how the carbon and hydrogen atoms are held together in a molecule of ethane.

....

....

....

....

[2]

[Total 4 marks]

5 The atoms in hydrogen sulfide (H_2S) are bonded in a similar way to the atoms in water (H_2O). **Grade 7-9**

Draw a dot and cross diagram of hydrogen sulfide. Only show the outer electrons of each atom.

[Total 2 marks]

Score:

14

Covalent Substances

1   The table below shows the properties of four substances.

Substance	Melting point (°C)	Conducts electricity when a liquid
A	−102	no
B	1085	yes
C	993	yes
D	1650	no

Which substance could be silicon dioxide, a giant covalent substance? Explain your answer.

....

....

[Total 2 marks]

2   Silicon carbide has a giant covalent structure and is a solid at room temperature.
Explain, in terms of its bonding and structure, why silicon carbide has a high melting point.

....

....

[Total 2 marks]

3   Three different carbon structures, **A**, **B** and **C**, are shown below.

a) Name each of the structures labelled **A** - **C**.

A ....   B ....   C ....

[3]

b) Explain how the bonding in structures **A** and **C** affects their electrical conductivity and hardness.

....

....

....

....

[4]

c) **A** and **B** both sublime. Explain why a sample of **B** would sublime at a lower temperature than **A**.

....

....

....

[3]   **Score:**

[Total 10 marks]

14

Electrical Conductivity and Metals

1   An experiment was carried out to find out if the ionic compound magnesium chloride conducts electricity. The compound was tested when it was solid, dissolved in water and molten.   Grade 4-6

a) Complete the table of results.

State	Conducts electricity? (yes/no)
Solid	....
Dissolved in water	....
Molten	....

[3]

b) Explain your answers to part a).

....

....

....

[2]

c) Explain why most covalent compounds don't conduct electricity.

....

....

[2]

[Total 7 marks]

2   Metals are held together by metallic bonding.   Grade 6-7

a) Draw a labelled diagram to show how the metal ions and the electrons that take part in bonding are arranged in a metal.

[3]

b) Metals are good conductors of electricity and most are malleable. Explain how the structure you drew in part a) gives metals these properties.

....

....

[2]

[Total 5 marks]

Score: [   ]

12

Balancing Equations

1 Carbon monoxide can form in poorly-ventilated gas fires.
Below is an equation for this reaction, which is incorrectly balanced.

$$C + O_2 \rightarrow CO$$

Which one of the following equations is balanced correctly?

☐ **A** $C + O_2 \rightarrow CO_2$　　　　☐ **C** $2C + O_2 \rightarrow 2CO$

☐ **B** $C + O_2 \rightarrow 2CO$　　　　☐ **D** $C + 2O_2 \rightarrow 4CO$

[Total 1 mark]

2 Methane (CH_4) burns in oxygen (O_2) to make carbon dioxide (CO_2) and water (H_2O).

a) Write a word equation for this reaction.

....

[1]

b) Write a **balanced** chemical equation for this reaction.

....

[2]

[Total 3 marks]

3 A more reactive halogen can displace a less reactive halogen from a solution of its salt.

Write a **balanced** chemical equation for the reaction of chlorine (Cl_2) with potassium bromide (KBr). The products of this reaction are bromine (Br_2) and potassium chloride (KCl).

....

[Total 2 marks]

4 Acids can react with a variety of different metals and their oxides.

a) Balance the following chemical equations.

i)　........HCl　+　........CuO　→　........$CuCl_2$　+　........H_2O

ii)　........HNO_3　+　........MgO　→　........$Mg(NO_3)_2$　+　........H_2O

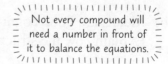

[2]

b) Write a **balanced** chemical equation for the reaction of hydrochloric acid (HCl) with aluminium (Al) that produces aluminium chloride ($AlCl_3$) and hydrogen (H_2).

....

[2]

[Total 4 marks]

5 Reduction reactions involve the removal of oxygen from a compound.

a) Balance the following equation, which shows the reduction of copper oxide.

$$........CuO + ...C \rightarrow ....Cu + ...CO_2$$

[1]

b) Balance the following equation, which shows the reduction of iron oxide.

$$........CO + ...Fe_2O_3 \rightarrow ....CO_2 + ...Fe$$

[1]

[Total 2 marks]

6 Sodium (Na) is a reactive alkali metal, which is found in Group 1 of the periodic table.

a) Sodium reacts with chlorine (Cl_2) to form sodium chloride (NaCl).

Write a **balanced** chemical equation for this reaction.

....

[2]

b) When a solution of calcium hydroxide ($Ca(OH)_2$) is mixed with solid sodium carbonate (Na_2CO_3), sodium hydroxide solution (NaOH) and a precipitate of calcium carbonate ($CaCO_3$) are produced.

The equation for the reaction is:

$$Ca(OH)_2(........) + Na_2CO_3(........) \rightarrow 2NaOH(........) + CaCO_3(........)$$

Complete the equation by adding state symbols.

[1]

c) Solid sodium metal reacts with water to form a solution of sodium hydroxide (NaOH). Hydrogen (H_2) is also given off.

Write a **balanced** chemical equation for this reaction, including state symbols.

....

[3]

[Total 6 marks]

7 Balance the following symbol equation to show how sulfur reacts with nitric acid.

$$........S + ...HNO_3 \rightarrow ....H_2SO_4 + ...NO_2 + ...H_2O$$

[Total 1 mark]

Exam Practice Tip	**Score**
It's important that you get to grips with balancing equations because it often features in exam papers. Remember to double check your equation after you've balanced it and you'll be on to a winner. You need to make sure you know your state symbols too, because they come hand-in-hand with chemical equations.	**19**

Section 3 — Equations, Calculations and Electrolysis

Relative Formula Mass

1 Which of the following compounds has a relative formula mass of 62?

   ☐ **A** sodium chloride, NaCl

   ☐ **B** potassium bromide, KBr

   ☑ **C** magnesium fluoride, MgF_2

   ☐ **D** sodium bromide, NaBr

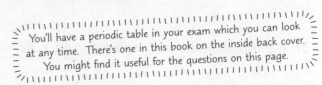
You'll have a periodic table in your exam which you can look at any time. There's one in this book on the inside back cover. You might find it useful for the questions on this page.

[Total 1 mark]

2 A solution of calcium hydroxide, $Ca(OH)_2$ can be known as limewater.

Calculate the relative formula mass of calcium hydroxide, $Ca(OH)_2$.

$$40 + (16 \times 2) + (2 \times 1) = 74$$

relative formula mass = ...**74**................

[Total 2 marks]

3 The formula of the compound zinc cyanide is $Zn(CN)_2$.

Calculate the relative formula mass of zinc cyanide.

$$65 + (2 \times 2 + 14 \times 2 = 117$$

relative formula mass = ...**117**................

[Total 2 marks]

4 The equation below shows a reaction between an unknown element, **A**, and water. The total M_r of the products is 114.

$$2A + 2H_2O \rightarrow \underbrace{2AOH + H_2} = 114$$

Identify element **A**.

$$2 \times A \times 17 \quad 36 \rightarrow 32A$$
$$34A *2$$

$$18 \times 2 = 36$$
$$2 \times A + 36$$

$$2A + 36 \rightarrow 2(A + 17) + 2$$
$$2A + 36 \rightarrow 2A + 34$$

Element A = ...**K**................

[Total 3 marks]

Score: ☐

8

Moles

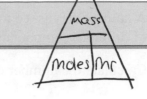

1 A scientist measured out one mole of iron into a beaker. What is the mass of one mole of iron?

 Grade 3-4

☐ **A** 56 g   ☐ **B** 26 kg   ☐ **C** 26 g   ☑ **D** 56 kg

[Total 1 mark]

2 Calculate the number of moles in 9.0 g of carbon.

 Grade 4-6

The relative atomic mass, A_r, of C = 12.

$$\frac{9.0}{12}$$

number of moles = 0.75

[Total 1 mark]

3 A pharmacist is synthesising aspirin, $C_9H_8O_4$, as part of a drugs trial. After the experiment, the pharmacist calculates that she has made 12.4 moles of aspirin. What mass of aspirin has the pharmacist made?

 Grade 4-6

The relative atomic mass, A_r, of C = 12, of H = 1 and of O = 16.

$$12.4 \times 180 = 2232$$

$$C_9H_8O_4 = 12 \times 9 + 8 * 16 \times 4 = 180$$

mass = 2232 g

[Total 2 marks]

4 A scientist finds a sample vial whilst clearing out a cupboard in the lab. The label on the vial says that it contains 0.075 moles of an unknown metal oxide.

 Grade 6-7

a) The sample weighs 3.0 g. Calculate the M_r of the metal oxide.

$$\frac{3.0}{0.075} = 40$$

M_r = 40 g

[1]

b) Which of these compounds could be the metal oxide?

☐ **A** Fe_2O_3 ☑ **B** MgO   ☐ **C** CaO   ☐ **D** Na_2O

[1]

[Total 2 marks]

 Section 3 — Equations, Calculations and Electrolysis

5 A student was asked to calculate the number of moles and the masses of different compounds she would be using in her lab practical.

a) Calculate the number of moles in 275 g of zinc carbonate ($ZnCO_3$).

number of moles = ...

[2]

b) Calculate the mass of 6 moles of hydrochloric acid (HCl).

mass = ... g

[2]

[Total 4 marks]

6 In a reaction between iron and oxygen, 3.52 kg of iron oxide is formed. The equation for the reaction is shown below.

$$4Fe + 3O_2 \rightarrow 2Fe_2O_3$$

Calculate the number of moles of iron oxide formed in this reaction.

$3.52 \times 1,000 = 3,520$

$\dfrac{3,520}{160} = 22$

$2 \times 112 \times 48 = 10,752$

$5,376$

$Fe_2O_3 = (56 \times 2) + (16 \times 3) = 160$

number of moles = ...**22**...

[Total 3 marks]

7 A teacher has a 140 g sample of potassium hydroxide (KOH).

Calculate how many more grams of KOH the teacher needs to have a 4 mole sample.

$KOH = 39 + 16 + 1 = 56$

$\dfrac{140}{56} = 2.5 \qquad 4 - 2.5 = 1.5$

$1.5 \times 56 = 84$

Extra KOH needed = ...**84**... g

[Total 2 marks]

Score:

15

Section 3 — Equations, Calculations and Electrolysis

Calculating Masses in Reactions

1 A student is investigating the combustion of metals.

a) The student burns 12 g of magnesium in air to produce magnesium oxide (MgO).

$$2Mg + O_2 \rightarrow 2MgO$$

Calculate the maximum mass of magnesium oxide that could be produced in the reaction.

Number of moles of Mg = $\frac{12}{24}$ = 0.5

This gives 0.5 moles of MgO

= 0.5 × (24+16) = 20

Mass of magnesium oxide = ...20........ g

[3]

b) Using the chemical equation below, work out the mass of sodium
that the student would need to burn in order to produce 6.2 g of sodium oxide.

$$4Na + O_2 \rightarrow 2Na_2O$$

0.2 mols of sodium

0.2 × 23 = 4.6

$Mr(Na_2O)$ = (23×2) +16

= 62g

× 2

Number of moles = $\frac{6.2}{62}$ = 0.1 mols

Mass of sodium – ....4.6........ g

[3]

[Total 6 marks]

2 Aluminium and iron oxide (Fe_2O_3) react to produce aluminium oxide (Al_2O_3) and iron.

$$2Al + Fe_2O_3 \rightarrow Al_2O_3 + 2Fe$$

a) What is the maximum mass of iron that can be produced from 20 g of iron oxide?

Mr for Fe_2O_3 = (56×2)+(16×3) = 160 $\frac{20}{160}$ = 0.125 ─×2 = 0.25 mols of iron (Fe)

0.25 × 56 = 914

Mass of iron = ... g

[3]

b) What is the maximum mass of aluminium that will react with 32.0 kg of iron oxide?

32 × 1,000 = 32,000/160 = 200 mols of iron oxide (Fe_2O_3)

200×2 = 400

Don't get caught out by changes in the units — part a) was in g, but part b) is in kg.

400×27 = 10,800 ÷ 1,000 = 10.8

Mass of aluminium = ... kg

[3]

[Total 6 marks]

Section 3 — Equations, Calculations and Electrolysis

3 Sodium sulfate (Na_2SO_4) is made by reacting sodium hydroxide (NaOH) with sulfuric acid (H_2SO_4). Water is another product of this reaction.

$$2NaOH + H_2SO_4 \rightarrow Na_2SO_4 + 2H_2O$$

a) What mass of sodium hydroxide is needed to make 71 g of sodium sulfate?

Mass of sodium hydroxide = ... g

[3]

b) What is the maximum mass of water that can be formed when 24.5 g of sulfuric acid reacts with sodium hydroxide?

Mass of water = ... g

[3]

[Total 6 marks]

4 Iron oxide is reduced to iron inside a blast furnace using carbon. There are three stages involved. The equations for these three stages are shown below.

Stage 1: $C_{(s)} + O_{2(g)} \rightarrow CO_{2(g)}$

Stage 2: $CO_{2(g)} + C_{(s)} \rightarrow 2CO_{(g)}$

Stage 3: $3CO_{(g)} + Fe_2O_{3(s)} \rightarrow 3CO_{2(g)} + 2Fe_{(l)}$

If 10.2 g of carbon are used in stage 2, and all the carbon monoxide produced gets used in stage 3, what mass of CO_2 is produced in stage 3?

Mass of CO_2 = ... g

[Total 5 marks]

Exam Practice Tip

It's really important to get your head around the method for calculating masses in reactions. It's just a case of finding the relative molecular masses for the bits that you want, and then doing a spot of dividing and multiplying. And don't forget to double check your working to make sure your answer is right.

Score

23

Calculating Percentage Yield

1 A teacher wanted to produce some silver chloride (AgCl). The teacher added a carefully measured mass of silver nitrate to an excess of dilute hydrochloric acid. 1.2 g of silver chloride were produced.

a) Explain what is meant by the **yield** of a chemical reaction.

....

[1]

b) The teacher calculated that he should get 1.6 g of silver chloride from the reaction. What was the percentage yield?

Percentage yield = ... %

[1]

[Total 2 marks]

2 Solutions of barium chloride and sodium sulfate were mixed together in a beaker to produce barium sulfate. The solution was filtered to obtain the solid barium sulfate.

The reaction was predicted to give a yield of 15 g of barium sulfate. However, after the experiment was completed a yield of only 6 g had been obtained. Calculate the percentage yield.

Percentage yield = ... %

[Total 1 mark]

3 When heated, calcium carbonate decomposes to form calcium oxide and carbon dioxide. The equation for the reaction is: $CaCO_3 \rightarrow CaO + CO_2$

In an industrial reaction, 68.00 kg of calcium carbonate decomposed to form 28.56 kg of calcium oxide, CaO. Calculate the percentage yield of calcium oxide.

Percentage yield = ... %

[Total 5 marks]

Score:

8

Section 3 — Equations, Calculations and Electrolysis

Empirical and Molecular Formulae

1 Nitrogen monoxide, NO, reacts with oxygen, O_2, to form oxide **R**.

A 100 g sample of oxide **R** contains 30.4 g of nitrogen and 69.6 g of oxygen.
Work out the empirical formula of oxide **R**.

Empirical formula = ...

[Total 3 marks]

2 A compound contains 10.1% aluminium and 89.9% bromine by mass.

Calculate the empirical formula of the compound.

Empirical formula = ...

[Total 3 marks]

3 1.48 g of a calcium compound contains 0.8 g calcium and 0.64 g of oxygen. The rest is hydrogen.

Work out the empirical formula of the compound.

Empirical formula = ...

[Total 4 marks]

4 A molecule has an empirical formula of C_3H_7O, and a relative molecular mass of 118.

Deduce the molecular formula of the molecule.

Molecular formula = ...

[Total 3 marks]

Score:

13

Section 3 — Equations, Calculations and Electrolysis

Finding Formulae Using Experiments

1   A student is carrying out a reaction to find the formula of an oxide of manganese. His experimental set-up is shown on the right.

burning gas
clamp
oxide of manganese
gas
Bunsen burner

Grade 4-6   **PRACTICAL**

a)   What is the name given to this type of reaction?

☐   **A** neutralisation

☐   **B** combustion

☐   **C** reduction

☐   **D** polymerisation

[1]

b)   During the reaction, manganese and oxygen are produced.
Some of the student's results are shown in the table.

mass of test tube and bung	36.48 g
mass of test tube and bung + manganese	84.88 g

i)   Calculate the mass of manganese present in the sample.

mass of manganese = ... g
[1]

ii) The mass of oxygen present was 14.08 g. Calculate the empirical formula of the oxide.
$A_r(Mn) = 55$, $A_r(O) = 16$

empirical formula = ...
[3]

[Total 5 marks]

2   A student carried out an experiment to calculate the empirical formula of an oxide of iron. She burnt 3.808 g of iron until it had all reacted. She found that the mass of the product was 5.440 g.

Grade 7-9   **PRACTICAL**

a)   Suggest a piece of equipment that the student could use to carry out the reaction in.

....
[1]

b)   Calculate the empirical formula of the iron oxide formed during the experiment.
$A_r(Fe) = 56$, $A_r(O) = 16$

empirical formula = ...
[4]

[Total 5 marks]

Score:
10

Water of Crystallisation

1 $Na_2CO_3.xH_2O$ is a hydrated salt, which means that water molecules are present in the lattice structure. This water is called water of crystallisation.

By heating a sample of a hydrated salt you can gradually remove the water of crystallisation to form an anhydrous salt. This can be done by placing a sample of the hydrated salt into a crucible and gently heating it using a Bunsen burner.

A student used this method to remove the water of crystallisation from $Na_2CO_3.xH_2O$ to produce the anhydrous salt Na_2CO_3. The student put a sample of $Na_2CO_3.xH_2O$ into a crucible, weighed both together, and recorded the mass. The student then heated the sample for 2 minutes, left it to cool and recorded the mass of the sample and crucible again. The student repeated this until two separate masses that had the same value were recorded. The student made a note of this mass.

The student recorded the following masses:

Starting mass of crucible + $Na_2CO_3.xH_2O$	61.224 g
Final mass of crucible + Na_2CO_3	56.364 g

a) What is the purpose of heating the hydrated salt until the mass remains constant?

....

[1]

b) The mass of the crucible was 53.500 g.
Use this to calculate the masses of the following samples.

   i) $Na_2CO_3.xH_2O$

....

[1]

   ii) Na_2CO_3

....

[1]

c) Use your answers to part b) to work out the value of x in $Na_2CO_3.xH_2O$.
(M_r H_2O = 18)

x = ...

[4]

[Total 7 marks]

Score:

7

Moles and Concentration

1 A student had a solution of an alkali with an unknown concentration. He also had some hydrochloric acid (HCl) at a concentration of 1.00 mol/dm³.

a) The student carried out an experiment to find out how much hydrochloric acid was needed to neutralise the alkali. He did the experiment 3 times and his results are shown in the table below. Calculate the mean volume of hydrochloric acid that was needed.

	Experiment Number		
	1	2	3
Volume of 1.00 mol/dm³ HCl (cm³)	12.50	12.55	12.45

Mean volume = ... cm³

[2]

b) Use your answer to part a) to calculate the number of moles of hydrochloric acid that reacted.

Number of moles = ...

[2]

[Total 4 marks]

2 Sodium hydroxide (NaOH) reacts with sulfuric acid to produce sodium sulfate (Na₂SO₄) and water.

a) How many moles of sodium hydroxide are in 120 cm³ of a 2.5 mol/dm³ solution?

Number of moles = ...

[1]

b) What is the concentration of a solution with 3 moles of sodium sulfate in 750 cm³?

Concentration = ... mol/dm³

[1]

c) Give your answer for part b) in g/dm³.

Concentration = ... g/dm³

[2]

[Total 4 marks]

Score: ☐

8

 ☐   ☐   ☐

Section 3 — Equations, Calculations and Electrolysis

Calculating Volume

1 The volume that one mole of a gas occupies is called its molar volume. **Grade 4-6**

a) State the value of the molar volume of a gas at room temperature and pressure.

....
.... *[1]*

b) What volume does 1.5 moles of hydrogen take up at room temperature and pressure?

Volume = ... dm³
[1]

[Total 2 marks]

2 How many moles are there in 2250 cm³ of ammonia (NH_3)? **Grade 4-6**

Number of moles = ...
[Total 1 mark]

3 A scientist completely burns 7.8 g of nitric oxide in oxygen. The equation for the reaction is: $2NO + O_2 \rightarrow 2NO_2$ **Grade 7-9**

a) Calculate the volume of nitrogen dioxide produced (at room temperature and pressure).

Volume = ... dm³
[3]

b) Find the volume of oxygen that reacted (at room temperature and pressure).

Volume = ... dm³
[2]

[Total 5 marks]

Score:

8

Section 3 — Equations, Calculations and Electrolysis

Electrolysis

1 The diagram below shows the electrolysis of lead bromide. **Grade 4-6**

a) Which substance is represented
in the diagram by the letter **W**?

☐ **A** Br$_2$ ☐ **C** molten lead

☐ **B** Br$^-$ ☐ **D** Pb^{2+}

[1]

b) Which substance is represented
in the diagram by the letter **X**?

☐ **A** Br$_2$ ☐ **C** molten lead

☐ **B** Br$^-$ ☐ **D** Pb^{2+}

[1]

c) Which substance is represented by the letter **Y** in the diagram?

☐ **A** Br$_2$ ☐ **B** Br$^-$ ☐ **C** molten lead   ☐ **D** Pb^{2+}

[1]

d) Which substance is represented by the letter **Z** in the diagram?

☐ **A** Br$_2$ ☐ **B** Br   ☐ **C** molten lead   ☐ **D** Pb^{2+}

[1]

[Total 4 marks]

2 Write balanced half-equations for the reactions occurring in the electrolysis of lead bromide. **Grade 6-7**

Negative electrode: ....

Positive electrode: ....

[Total 4 marks]

3 A student carries out the electrolysis of molten potassium iodide. **Grade 6-7**

a) Name the substance that will form at the:

Negative electrode: ....   Positive electrode: ....

[2]

b) Is the reaction at the positive electrode an example of oxidation or reduction? Explain your answer.

....

[1]

[Total 3 marks]

Score: ☐

11

 ☐   ☐   ☐   Section 3 — Equations, Calculations and Electrolysis

Electrolysis of Aqueous Solutions

1 Electrolysis using inert electrodes can be carried out with several different aqueous solutions. Grade 4-6

a) Balance the following half-equations for the reactions that occur during the electrolysis of an aqueous solution of sodium chloride.

$$........H^+ \ + \ ....e^- \ \rightarrow \ ....H_2$$

$$........Cl^- \ \rightarrow \ ....Cl_2 \ + \ ....e^-$$

[2]

b) Balance the following half-equation for the reaction that occurs at the anode during the electrolysis of an aqueous solution of dilute sulfuric acid.

$$........OH^- \ \rightarrow \ ....O_2 \ + \ ....H_2O \ + \ ....e^-$$

[1]

c) During the electrolysis of aqueous silver chloride, silver ions are reduced to silver metal. At which electrode would you expect this reaction to occur?

....

[1]

[Total 4 marks]

2 Electrolysis is carried out on a solution of copper chloride, $CuCl_2$, using inert electrodes. Grade 6-7

a) Which of the following ions is **not** present in the solution?

☐ **A** H^+

☐ **B** H_2O^-

☐ **C** Cu^{2+}

☐ **D** Cl^-

Questions testing your knowledge of the formula and charges of common ions are bound to come up in the exam — make sure you learn them.

[1]

b) Suggest a material that the inert electrodes could be made from.

....

[1]

c) What would you expect to see happen at:

i) the anode? ....

ii) the cathode? ....

[2]

[Total 4 marks]

3   A student investigated the products of electrolysis of a variety of aqueous solutions using inert electrodes.   (Grade 7-9)   **PRACTICAL**

a) Draw a **labelled** diagram of suitable apparatus that could be used for these experiments.

[3]

Paper 2

b) An aqueous solution of copper sulfate ($CuSO_4$) can undergo electrolysis.

i) State the **four** ions that this solution contains.

1 ....   2 ....

3 ....   4 ....

[4]

ii) Copper is produced in a reaction at one of the electrodes during the electrolysis of this solution. Write the half-equation for this reaction.

....

[2]

c) When potassium nitrate solution is electrolysed neither potassium nor nitrogen are discharged. Explain why and state what is produced instead.

....

....

....

....

[4]

[Total 13 marks]

Exam Practice Tip

Remember, when you electrolyse aqueous solutions (rather than molten salts), what products are made depends on the reactivity of all the ions in solution. Make sure you know how to predict which ions will be discharged from a solution. And get plenty of practice at writing half-equations too — they're dead important...

Score

[ ]

21

Section 3 — Equations, Calculations and Electrolysis

Group 1 — The Alkali Metals

1   A teacher dropped small, similar sized pieces of three different alkali metals, **A**, **B** and **C**, into water. The students recorded the time taken for each piece to react completely.

Metal	Time taken to react (s)
A	27
B	8
C	42

a) State which of these metals, **A**, **B** or **C**, is the most reactive. Explain how you know.

....

....

                                                                                                                        [2]

b) The three metals used were lithium, sodium and potassium.
    Use the results shown in the table to match them up to the correct letters **A**, **B** and **C**.

    A = ...   **B** = ...   **C** = ...
                                                                                                                        [2]

c) What products would be formed in a reaction between sodium and water?

....

                                                                                                                        [2]

d) One of the students said "The amount of time taken for rubidium to react with water
    would be shorter than for metal **A**, but longer than for metal **B**".

    Why is the student incorrect?

....

....

                                                                                                                        [2]
                                                                                                            [Total 8 marks]

2   Explain why alkali metals become more reactive as their atomic number increases.

....

....

....
                                                                                                            [Total 3 marks]

Paper 2

Exam Practice Tip

Chemistry is full of patterns, so if you come across one make sure you learn the reason behind it — not only will it help you to remember the pattern, it might well get you some marks in the exam. If you're doing Paper 2, one to make sure you know is the reason why reactivity changes as you go down a group.

Score

11

Group 7 — The Halogens

1   The properties of the elements within Group 7 change as you go down the group.

a)   Complete the table to show the colour of chlorine and the physical state of iodine at 25 °C.

Element	Atomic number	Colour	Boiling point (°C)	Physical state at 25 °C
chlorine	17	....	−34	gas
bromine	35	red-brown	59	liquid
iodine	53	dark grey	185	....

[2]

b)   Fluorine is another Group 7 element.

i)   How would you expect the reactivity of fluorine to compare to the reactivity of chlorine?

....

[1]

ii)   Predict the physical state of fluorine at 25 °C.

....

[1]

[Total 4 marks]

2   The reactivity of halogens is dependent on their electronic configuration.

a)   Describe the electronic configuration of the halogens and how it changes down Group 7.

....

....

....

[2]

b)   Sodium reacts violently with fluorine, at room temperature, to form sodium fluoride.
Predict how astatine might react with sodium at room temperature. Explain your answer.

....

....

....

....

....

[4]

[Total 6 marks]

Score: ☐

10

Section 4 — Inorganic Chemistry

Displacement Reactions

1 Halogens can take part in displacement reactions with halogen salts. For example, bromine water will react with potassium iodide solution.

Grade 4-6

a) State what is meant by the term **displacement reaction**.

....

....

[1]

b) The reaction of bromine water with potassium iodide is a redox reaction. The equation for the reaction is:

$$Br_{2(aq)} + 2KI_{(aq)} \rightarrow 2KBr_{(aq)} + I_{2(aq)}$$

i) State what is meant by the term **redox reaction**.

....

....

[1]

ii) Which substance is being oxidised in the reaction above?

....

[1]

iii) Which substance is being reduced in the reaction above?

....

[1]

If you're struggling with parts b) ii) and iii), try using the balanced equation to help you work out what's losing electrons and what's gaining electrons.

[Total 4 marks]

2 When chlorine water is added to a solution of potassium iodide, a chemical reaction occurs.

Grade 6-7

a) State the colour of the solution before and after the reaction.

Before ....

After ....

[2]

b) Astatine is below iodine in Group 7. Predict whether chlorine water would react with sodium astatide solution. Explain your answer.

....

....

[2]

[Total 4 marks]

Score: ☐

8

Gases in the Atmosphere

1   This pie chart shows the composition of the Earth's atmosphere, excluding water vapour.   *Grade 4-6*

   a)   Complete the labels on the pie chart.

carbon dioxide

i) .... *[1]*

ii) .... *[1]*

iii) .... *[1]*

   b)   Give the approximate percentages of the following gases in the air:

     i) nitrogen ....   ii) carbon dioxide ....

                [1]   *[1]*

                                                                  [Total 5 marks]

2   A student sets up an experiment to investigate what percentage of the air is made up of oxygen. The apparatus used is shown on the right.   *Grade 6-7*   **PRACTICAL**

iron wool soaked in acetic acid

air

water

     As the iron reacts with the oxygen in the air to make iron oxide, the water in the tube rises to fill the space the oxygen took up. The student marked the starting and finishing level of water on the test tube using a pen. To find the volume of air in the test tube at the start and end of the experiment, she filled the tube with water up to each mark and poured that water into a measuring cylinder. The volume of water was equivalent to the volume of air in the test tube.

   a)   The student found that at the beginning of the experiment the test tube contained 28.0 cm³ of air. At the end of the experiment the test tube contained 21.7 cm³ of air.

     Use these results to calculate the percentage of oxygen in air.

                                Percentage of oxygen in air = ... %

                                                                         [2]

   b)   Suggest **one** change to the apparatus that would improve the accuracy of the student's results. Explain your answer.

     ....

     ....

     ....

                                                                  [2]

                                                                [Total 4 marks]

Score: [   ]

9

Gases in Reactions

1   Heating a metal carbonate, such as copper(II) carbonate, produces carbon dioxide.

a) i) Complete the equation below for the reaction that occurs when copper(II) carbonate is heated.

$$CuCO_{3(s)} \rightarrow \text{...........}_{(s)} + CO_{2(g)}$$

[1]

ii) Suggest a method for collecting the carbon dioxide gas produced by this reaction.

....

....

[1]

b) What is the name for the type of reaction where a substance is heated and breaks down
to produce two or more products?

....

[1]

[Total 3 marks]

2   Some elements burn in air to produce oxides.

a) i) State the colour of the flame from the combustion reaction of sulfur.

....

[1]

ii) The product formed from the combustion reaction of sulfur can be dissolved in water.
State the acid-base characteristic of the resulting solution.

....

[1]

b) Magnesium can also be burnt to form an oxide.
Describe what you would see when magnesium is burnt in air.

....

....

[2]

c) Give the balanced symbol equation for the combustion of hydrogen in air.

....

[2]

[Total 6 marks]

Exam Practice Tip

In your exams, you may need to apply the knowledge of the reactions you've learnt to other situations.
For example, you may be given a reaction with an unfamiliar carbonate and asked what the products will be.
Don't panic, just look at the reactants and think whether you have seen a similar reaction before.

Score

9

Carbon Dioxide

1 Carbon dioxide is a greenhouse gas. (Grade 4-6)

a) This experiment was used to compare the effects of nitrogen and carbon dioxide on heat radiation.

carbon dioxide gas   heat source   nitrogen gas

heat detector **A**   clear plastic tubes (do not block heat radiation)   heat detector **B**

State which detector, **A** or **B**, will detect more heat from the heat source. Explain your choice.

....

....

[2]

b) Explain the effect of atmospheric carbon dioxide on heat radiated from the Earth's surface.

....

....

[2]

[Total 4 Marks]

2 The graphs below show how the atmospheric CO_2 level and temperature changed over time. (Grade 6-7)

% CO_2 in the atmosphere

0.034
0.032
0.030
0.028

Year
1850   1900   1950   2000

Average temperature (°C)

15.50
15.00
14.50

Year
1850   1900   1950   2000

a) Describe the trends in the data and suggest reasons for them.

....

....

....

....

[4]

b) State **one** possible effect of the trend in the Earth's temperature.

....

[1]

[Total 5 marks]

Score: ☐

9

Reactions of Metals

1   A student performed some experiments  to investigate the reactivity of metals.

a)   First, the student placed pieces of four different metals into dilute hydrochloric acid. The diagram below shows what the four experiments looked like after 1 minute.

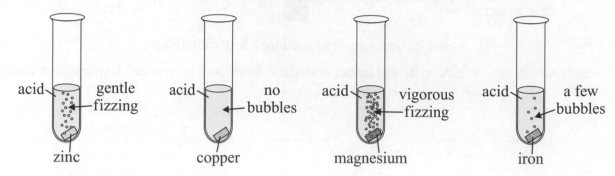

Use the information in the diagram to put these metals in order of reactivity.

Most reactive: ....

....

....

Least reactive: ....

[2]

b)   Next, the student was given samples of three mystery metals, marked **X**, **Y** and **Z**. She put small pieces of each of the metals in cold water. If there was no reaction with cold water, she tested the metal to see if it would react with steam. Her results are shown in the table below.

Metal	Any reaction with cold water?	Any reaction with steam?
X	Reacts vigorously. Hydrogen gas is produced.	
Y	no reaction	Reacts vigorously. Metal is coated with a white solid. Hydrogen gas is produced.
Z	no reaction	no reaction

i)   Metal **Y** was zinc. It reacted with the steam to produce hydrogen gas and a white solid. Name the white solid that was produced by this reaction.

....

[1]

ii)   One of the other metals the student was given was sodium. Suggest whether sodium was metal **X** or metal **Z**. Give a reason for your answer.

....

....

[1]

[Total 4 marks]

2 A student investigated the reactions of some metals and found the results shown in the table below.

Reaction	Observation
Lithium + water	Very vigorous reaction with fizzing, lithium disappears
Calcium + water	Fizzing, calcium disappears
Magnesium + water	No fizzing, a few bubbles on the magnesium
Copper + water	No fizzing, no change to copper
Iron + water	No fizzing, no change to iron
Lithium + dilute acid	Very vigorous reaction with fizzing, lithium disappears
Magnesium + dilute acid	Fizzing, magnesium disappears
Zinc + dilute acid	Fizzing, zinc disappears
Copper + dilute acid	No fizzing, no change to copper

a) Magnesium reacts with dilute sulfuric acid to form magnesium sulfate.
   Give the balanced symbol equation for this reaction.

   ....
   [2]

b) Predict what the student would have seen if they had added sodium to water.

   ....

   ....
   [2]

c) Put the metals calcium, copper and lithium in order from most reactive to least reactive.

   ....
   [1]

d) Explain why it would be difficult to decide the order of reactivity of magnesium and zinc using these experiments. Suggest an experiment that could be used to decide which is more reactive.

   ....

   ....

   ....
   [2]

   [Total 7 marks]

Exam Practice Tip

Make sure you understand what the reactions of metals with acids and water tell you about the reactivity of metals. There is no need to learn exactly the observations of all the metals with water and acids as long as you know the differences in their reactivity and how this affects how vigorous the reactions will be.

Score

[ ]

11

The Reactivity Series

1 A more reactive metal will displace a less reactive metal from a solution of its salt. *(Grade 3-4)*

a) Which of the following metals will displace aluminium from a solution of aluminium chloride?

- [ ] **A** zinc
- [ ] **B** calcium
- [ ] **C** copper
- [ ] **D** iron

Writing out the reactivity series on a spare bit of paper will help with this question.

[1]

b) Which of the following metals will displace iron from an aqueous solution of iron chloride?

- [ ] **A** silver
- [ ] **B** copper
- [ ] **C** gold
- [ ] **D** sodium

[1]

[Total 2 marks]

2 A student placed pieces of copper, zinc and an unknown metal in zinc sulfate solution and copper sulfate solution and left them for an hour. The student's results are shown below. *(Grade 4-6)*

	zinc	copper	unidentified metal
reaction with zinc sulfate	no reaction	no reaction	no reaction
reaction with copper sulfate	reaction	no reaction	reaction

a) Suggest the name of the unidentified metal.

....

[1]

b) Explain how you can tell that the unidentified metal is more reactive than copper.

....

[1]

c) Explain why there was no reaction between copper and zinc sulfate.

....

[1]

[Total 3 marks]

3 A student performed an investigation to observe the chemical reactions of four metals with some metal oxides. The student's results are displayed in the table below. The student put a tick if a reaction occurred and a cross if there was no reaction.

	aluminium oxide	copper oxide	iron oxide	magnesium oxide
aluminium	✗	✓	✓	✗
copper	✗	✗	✗	✗
iron				
magnesium	✓	✓	✓	✗

a) Complete the table to show the results for iron.

[2]

b) State how many of the oxides in the table you would expect to react with gold. ....

[1]

c) Which metal in the table would you expect to react most vigorously with copper oxide? Give a reason for your answer.

....

....

....

[2]

[Total 5 marks]

4 A student carries out a displacement reaction by reacting magnesium with an aqueous solution of iron(II) chloride ($FeCl_2$) to produce magnesium chloride and iron.

a) Write the balanced symbol equation for this reaction, including state symbols.

....

[2]

b) Explain why this displacement reaction is an example of a redox reaction.

....

....

[2]

c) Copper is a brown metal and copper(II) sulfate is blue in solution.
Aluminium is a shiny grey metal and aluminium sulfate is colourless in solution.

Predict the student's observations when aluminium is added to copper(II) sulfate.

....

....

[2]

[Total 6 marks]

Score:

16

Iron

1 In an experiment to investigate rusting, three iron nails were placed into separate test tubes. *Grade 4-6*

boiled (airless) water → **A**

air → tap water → **B**

air → cotton wool drying agent → **C**

a) State the **two** things that are needed for iron to rust.

1 .... 2 ....
[2]

b) In which tube, **A**, **B** or **C**, will the nail rust? ....
[1]

c) A fourth test tube was set up with identical conditions to **B**, but using a nail that had first been coated in paint. Suggest what you would observe in this test tube and explain your prediction.

....

....
[2]

[Total 5 marks]

2 There are several methods that can be used to prevent the corrosion of metals and alloys. *Grade 6-7*

a) A ship manufacturer wants to prevent the corrosion of a steel ship using sacrificial protection. Describe what is meant by sacrificial protection and explain how it protects the ship.

....

....

....

....
[3]

b) A roofing company coats an iron roof with a layer of zinc to protect it from rusting. After a while, the zinc layer becomes scratched. Would you expect the iron roofing to begin to rust? Explain your answer.

....

....
[2]

[Total 5 marks]

Exam Practice Tip

Learning what's required for rust to form is really important for answering questions on iron. Equally important is learning the ways that rust is prevented from forming in the real world. It's useful to remember how the reactivity series ties in to the sacrificial method of protection too.

Score

[ ]

10

Metals and Redox

1 Zinc oxide can be reduced to zinc using carbon. **Grade 4-6**

a) Write the word equation for this reaction.

....

[1]

b) Identify the reducing agent in this reaction.

....

[1]

[Total 2 marks]

2 Not all metals can be extracted using carbon.
Some need to be extracted using a different method. **Grade 4-6**

a) Give the name of the process used to extract these metals.

....

[1]

b) Explain why not all metals can be extracted using carbon.

....

....

[1]

[Total 2 marks]

3 Most metals are found as compounds in ores in the Earth's crust. **Grade 4-6**
Some of the metals can be extracted by heating their ores with carbon.

a) Why are most metals found in the earth as compounds?

....

[1]

b) Explain why iron can be extracted from iron oxide by heating with carbon.

....

....

[2]

c) Name the type of reaction that removes a metal from its ore. ....

[1]

d) Write a balanced symbol equation for the reaction of iron(III) oxide (Fe_2O_3) with carbon.

....

[2]

[Total 6 marks]

Score: ☐

10

 ☐   ☐   ☐

Paper 2

Uses of Metals

1   The table below shows some data about the properties of three alloys.

Alloy	Carbon Composition (%)	Strength (MPa)	Density (g/cm³)
Alloy 1 (stainless steel)	0.07	200	8.1
Alloy 2 (low carbon steel)	0.1	250	7.6
Alloy 3 (high carbon steel)	1.6	350	7.9

a) Use the data to describe the effect on strength of increasing the carbon content in steel.

....

....

[1]

b) Explain why alloys are generally harder than pure metals.

....

....

....

....

[3]

c) Stainless steel is often used to make kitchen equipment. Suggest a property of stainless steel, other than the properties shown in the table above, that makes it well suited for this use.

....

[1]

[Total 5 marks]

2   The different properties of iron and aluminium lead to differences in their uses.

Metals can be used in the construction of racing yachts.
Suggest which metal out of iron and aluminium would be most suitable for this use.
Explain your answer.

....

....

....

....

....

[Total 3 marks]

Score: ☐

8

Acids and Alkalis

1 The pH scale shows how acidic or alkaline substances are. **Grade 3-4**

a) What range of values does pH take? ....

[1]

b) What term is used to describe a substance with a pH of 7? ....

[1]

c) Caustic soda has a pH of around 13. Which of the following phrases best describes caustic soda?

☐ **A** Strong acid   ☐ **B** Strong alkali   ☐ **C** Weak acid   ☐ **D** Weak alkali

[1]

[Total 3 marks]

2 Bleach has a pH of around 12. **Grade 4-6**

Complete the table to show what colour it would turn the following indicators.

Indicator	Colour
Litmus paper	....
Phenolphthalein	....
Universal indicator	purple
Methyl orange	....

[Total 3 marks]

3 A student has a test tube containing some acid.
The student adds a few drops of Universal indicator to the acid and it turns red. **Grade 6-7**
The student then gradually adds some alkali to the test tube.

a) What type of ions in the acid cause the indicator to become red?

....

[1]

b) What type of reaction takes place between the acid and the alkali?

....

[1]

c) Write the equation for the reaction that occurs between the ions in the acid and the alkali.
Include state symbols in your answer.

....

[2]

[Total 4 marks]

Score: ☐

10

 ☐   ☐   ☐

Section 4 — Inorganic Chemistry

Reactions of Acids

1 Dilute acids can react with metals and with metal oxides. Complete the word equations for the reactions below. *(Grade 4-6)*

a) sulfuric acid + magnesium oxide → .... + ...

[1]

b) hydrochloric acid + aluminium → .... + ...

[1]

[Total 2 marks]

2 A student is investigating the reactions of acids. *(Grade 6-7)*

a) The student reacts nitric acid with copper oxide. Write a word equation for the reaction.

....

[1]

b) The student then adds zinc hydroxide, $Zn(OH)_2$, to a test tube of hydrochloric acid. Write a balanced symbol equation for the reaction.

....

[2]

c) The student then reacts sulfuric acid with aqueous ammonia. Name the salt that would form in this reaction.

....

[1]

[Total 4 marks]

3 When a spatula of magnesium carbonate powder ($MgCO_3$) is added to a test tube containing nitric acid (HNO_3), bubbles of gas are given off. *(Grade 6-7)*

a) Name the gas evolved during the reaction.

....

[1]

b) Write a balanced symbol equation for the reaction.

....

[2]

c) Some magnesium carbonate powder is left over. Suggest an appropriate acid that could be added to it to make magnesium chloride.

....

[1]

[Total 4 marks]

Score:

10

Section 4 — Inorganic Chemistry

Titrations

1 The concentration of some limewater, $Ca(OH)_2$ solution, was determined by titration with hydrochloric acid, HCl. 50 cm³ of limewater required 20 cm³ of 0.1 mol/dm³ hydrochloric acid to neutralise it.

The chemical equation for the reaction is: $Ca(OH)_2 + 2HCl \rightarrow CaCl_2 + 2H_2O$

a) Calculate the amount, in moles, of hydrochloric acid used in the reaction.

.... moles
[2]

b) Calculate how many moles of calcium hydroxide were used.

.... moles
[1]

c) Calculate the concentration of the limewater in mol/dm³.

Concentration = ... mol/dm³
[2]

d) Describe how the end-point of this reaction could be determined.

....

....
[2]

[Total 7 marks]

2 In a titration, 10.0 cm³ of sulfuric acid was used to neutralise 30.0 cm³ of 0.10 mol/dm³ potassium hydroxide solution. The equation for the reaction is:

$$H_2SO_4 + 2KOH \rightarrow K_2SO_4 + 2H_2O$$

a) Calculate the concentration of the sulfuric acid in mol/dm³.

Concentration = ... mol/dm³
[3]

b) Calculate the concentration of the sulfuric acid in g/dm³.

Concentration = ... g/dm³
[2]

[Total 5 marks]

Score: ⬜

12

Section 4 — Inorganic Chemistry

Making Insoluble Salts

1 Fill in the table below by stating whether the salt is soluble or insoluble.

Salt	Solubility
Silver chloride	....
Sodium nitrate	....
Magnesium hydroxide	....

[Total 3 marks]

2 A student is making a sample of lead sulfate, an insoluble salt, by mixing two salt solutions.

a) Suggest **two** salt solutions that the student could mix to make lead sulfate.

....

....

[1]

b) Once the student has made the salt, he pours the whole solid and salt solution into a filter funnel, as shown in the diagram below.

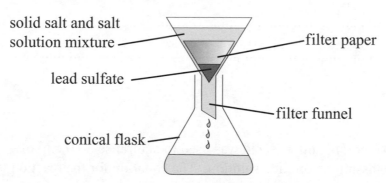

solid salt and salt solution mixture — filter paper

lead sulfate —

filter funnel

conical flask —

What has the student done wrong? Explain how this could affect the mass of solid salt that he collects from the solution.

....

....

....

[2]

c) In a second reaction, the student wants to produce the insoluble salt calcium carbonate, $CaCO_3$. Suggest **two** soluble salts he could react together to make a precipitate of calcium carbonate.

....

....

[2]

[Total 5 marks]

Score:

8

Making Soluble Salts

1 A student is making a sample of a salt by reacting ammonium hydroxide with hydrochloric acid. **Grade 4-6**

a) Name the salt formed in this reaction.

....

[1]

b) The student uses a titration method to add ammonium hydroxide solution to the acid until the reaction reaches its end point, which is shown by a change in colour of an indicator in the solution. The student then crystallises the solution to obtain the salt.
Will this produce a pure sample of the salt? Explain your answer.

....

....

[1]

[Total 2 marks]

2 Copper sulfate is a soluble salt that can be made by the reaction between sulfuric acid, H_2SO_4, and copper oxide, CuO. **Grade 7-9** **PRACTICAL**

a) Write a balanced chemical equation, including state symbols, for the reaction between sulfuric acid and copper oxide.

....

[2]

b) Outline how you could prepare a pure, dry sample of copper sulfate in the lab from sulfuric acid and copper oxide.

....

....

....

....

....

....

....

....

[6]

[Total 8 marks]

Exam Practice Tip

If you're lucky, you might get to make some soluble salts of your very own in class, but don't forget, you also need to know about how to make them for your exams. Make sure you go through the method a few times to make sure you understand what has to be done and why each stage is carried out before moving on.

Score

10

Section 4 — Inorganic Chemistry

Tests for Cations

1 Potassium chloride is used to replace some of the sodium chloride in low-sodium table salt. A flame test can be used to tell the difference between potassium chloride and sodium chloride.

Grade 6-7

a) Describe how to carry out a flame test.

....

....

....

[2]

b) Explain how you could tell from a flame test that a substance was potassium chloride and not sodium chloride.

....

....

[2]

[Total 4 marks]

2 A student adds a few drops of NaOH solution to solutions of different metal compounds.

Grade 6-7

a) i) Which solution releases ammonia when sodium hydroxide solution is added?

☐ **A** $CaCl_2$ ☐ **C** LiCl

☐ **B** $CuSO_4$ ☐ **D** $(NH_4)_2SO_4$

[1]

ii) Describe a chemical test for ammonia gas.

....

[1]

b) Which solution forms a blue precipitate with sodium hydroxide solution?

☐ **A** $CaCl_2$ ☐ **C** LiCl

☐ **B** $CuSO_4$ ☐ **D** $(NH_4)_2SO_4$

[1]

c) Complete the balanced ionic equation for the reaction of iron(II) ions with hydroxide ions by inserting state symbols.

$$Fe^{2+}_{(\ldots\ldots)} + 2OH^-_{(\ldots\ldots)} \rightarrow Fe(OH)_{2(\ldots\ldots)}$$

[1]

[Total 4 marks]

Score: ☐

8

Section 4 — Inorganic Chemistry

Tests for Anions

1 Complete the following symbol equation for the reactions involved in a negative ion test.

$$Ba^{2+} + \text{....................} \rightarrow BaSO_4$$

[Total 1 mark]

2 A student has a sample of an ionic compound and wants to test for the presence of different ions.

a) Give the chemical formula and charge of the negative ions present in the following compounds.

   i) magnesium carbonate .... *[1]*

   ii) potassium iodide .... *[1]*

b) i) State which **two** reactants are used to test for sulfate ions.

   Reactant 1 ....

   Reactant 2 ....

   [2]

   ii) What would be observed after adding these reactants to a solution of a sulfate compound?

   ....

   [1]

   [Total 5 marks]

3 A student is given a solution and told that it contains either chloride or carbonate ions. Describe how the student could test for each of these ions, and what the student would see in each case if the ions were present.

....

....

....

....

....

....

....

....

[Total 4 marks]

Score:

10

Tests for Gases and Water

1 Electrolysis of water gives hydrogen gas and oxygen gas. **Grade 4-6**

a) Describe a simple laboratory test that you could use to identify hydrogen gas.

....

....
[2]

b) Describe a simple laboratory test that you could use to identify oxygen gas.

....

....
[2]

[Total 4 marks]

2 A fuel was burnt in pure oxygen and the products of the combustion reaction were collected. **Grade 6-7**

a) A liquid condensed out of the products after they were cooled to room temperature.
The liquid was added to anhydrous copper(II) sulfate.
Describe the colour change that would be observed if the liquid contained water.

....
[2]

b) The test with anhydrous copper(II) sulfate indicated that the liquid contained water.
Next, the liquid's freezing point and boiling point were found.

   Freezing point: $-4\,°C$ **Boiling point:** $106\,°C$

   Explain what these results show.

....

....
[3]

c) The gas that was produced by the burning fuel was also tested. The gas did not bleach damp litmus paper. When the gas was bubbled through limewater, the limewater turned cloudy.

   Explain what these results show.

....

....

....
[4]

[Total 9 marks]

Score:

13

Energy Transfer in Reactions

1 Which of the following energy changes describes an exothermic reaction?

	Energy change of reaction	Temperature of surroundings
A	Takes in energy	Increases
B	Gives out energy	Increases
C	Takes in energy	Decreases
D	Gives out energy	Decreases

[Total 1 mark]

2 During the following reaction, the temperature of the reaction mixture decreases.

$$AB \;+\; C \;\rightarrow\; AC \;+\; B$$

a) State, with a reason, whether the reaction is exothermic or endothermic.

....

....

[2]

b) i) What is meant by the **enthalpy change** of a reaction?

....

[1]

ii) State whether the enthalpy change of the above reaction is positive or negative.

....

[1]

iii) Give the symbol that is used to represent enthalpy change.

....

[1]

[Total 5 marks]

3 The thermal decomposition of calcium carbonate is an endothermic reaction.

Sketch and label a reaction profile for this reaction on the axes below. Label the enthalpy change.

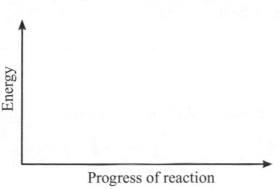

[Total 3 marks]

Score:

9

Paper 2

PRACTICAL Measuring Enthalpy Changes

1 A student measured the temperature change during a reaction between sodium hydroxide and hydrochloric acid using the apparatus shown below.

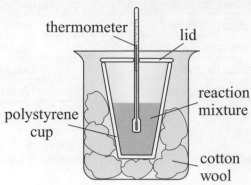

a) Before mixing the reagents, the student measured the temperature of each of them. Explain why.

....

[1]

b) State the purpose of:

i) the cotton wool ....

[1]

ii) the lid ....

[1]

c) The student measured the temperature over the first 30 seconds of the reaction. Her results are plotted on the graph shown on the right. What was the temperature increase during the reaction?

.... °C

[1]

d) What is the dependent variable in this experiment?

....

[1]

e) How could the reliability of the results be improved?

....

[1]

f) This is a neutralisation reaction.
Give **one** other type of reaction this method could be used to study. ....

[1]

[Total 7 marks]

Score:

7

Calculating Enthalpy Changes

1 A scientist conducted a calorimetry experiment to measure the energy produced when petrol is burnt. 0.7 g of petrol was burned in a spirit burner placed underneath a copper can containing 50 g of water. The temperature of the water increased by 30.5 °C.

Grade 6-7

a) Why was a copper can chosen to hold the water?

....
[1]

b) Calculate the heat energy change in the experiment.
The specific heat capacity of water is 4.2 J/g/°C.

Heat energy change = ... J
[2]

c) Use your answer to b) to calculate the energy produced per gram of petrol.
Give your answer in kJ/g.

Energy produced = ... kJ/g
[2]

[Total 5 marks]

2 A student found that burning 1.15 g of ethanol (C_2H_5OH) raised the temperature of 50 g of water by 34.5 °C. She calculated that this was a heat energy change of 7245 J.

Grade 7-9

a) Calculate the number of moles of ethanol that the student burnt in her experiment.

> To work out the number of moles, you first need to work out the relative formula mass.

Moles = ... mol
[2]

b) Calculate the molar enthalpy change (in kJ/mol) for the combustion of ethanol.

Molar enthalpy change = ... kJ/mol
[2]

[Total 4 marks]

Exam Practice Tip

Calculations, calculations, calculations. Everyone's favourite. You'll have heard it a thousand times before, but always <u>check your working</u> after you've done a question, and check the <u>units</u> too. For a molar enthalpy question you also need to think about <u>signs</u>: '-' for exothermic reactions and '+' for endothermic reactions.

Score

9

Section 5 — Physical Chemistry

Bond Energies

1 Calculate the enthalpy change during the combustion of methane, CH_4. Use the equation and bond energy information given below.

Bond	Energy (kJ/mol)
C–H	+412
O=O	+498
C=O	+743
O–H	+463

$$CH_4 + 2O_2 \rightarrow CO_2 + 2H_2O$$

Enthalpy change = ... kJ/mol

[Total 4 marks]

2 Hydrazine is a molecule with the formula N_2H_4.

a) Calculate the enthalpy change for the combustion of hydrazine. Use the equation and bond energy information given below.

Bond	Energy (kJ/mol)
N–N	+158
N–H	+391
O=O	+498
N≡N	+945
O–H	+463

$$N_2H_4 + O_2 \rightarrow N_2 + 2H_2O$$

Enthalpy change = ... kJ/mol

[4]

b) Using your answer to a), state whether the combustion of hydrazine is endothermic or exothermic. Explain your answer.

....

....

[2]

[Total 6 marks]

Score:

10

Rates of Reaction

1 This question is about the rate of a chemical reaction between two reactants, one of which is in solution, and one of which is a solid.

Grade 4-6

a) Which of the following changes would **not** cause the rate of the chemical reaction to increase?

☐ **A** Increasing the concentration of the solution.

☐ **B** Heating the reaction mixture to a higher temperature.

☐ **C** Using a larger volume of the solution, but keeping the concentration the same.

☐ **D** Grinding the solid reactant so that it forms a fine powder.

[1]

b) What is the name given to the minimum amount of energy which particles must have if they are to react when they collide?

....

[1]

[Total 2 marks]

2 The graph below shows how the mass of gas lost from a reaction vessel changes over time, for the same reaction under different conditions.

Grade 6-7

State and explain which of the reactions, **A**, **B** or **C**:

Produced the most product: ....

....

Finished first: ....

....

Started at the slowest rate: ....

....

[Total 6 marks]

Section 5 — Physical Chemistry

3 This question is about the rate of the reaction between magnesium and hydrochloric acid. The chemical equation for the reaction is:

$$Mg_{(s)} + 2HCl_{(aq)} \rightarrow MgCl_{2(aq)} + H_{2(g)}$$

a) The graph below shows how the volume of hydrogen produced changes over the course of the reaction when a small lump of magnesium is added to excess hydrochloric acid.

On the same axes, sketch a curve to show how the volume of hydrogen produced would change over time if an identical piece of magnesium was added to excess hydrochloric acid with a higher concentration.

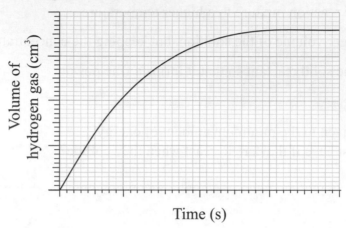

Time (s)

[2]

b) State **two** properties of the collisions between particles that affect the rate of a reaction.

....

[2]

c) Use collision theory to explain why increasing the concentration of a reactant increases the rate of the reaction.

....

....

[2]

d) How would you expect the reaction rate to change if the magnesium was cut into smaller pieces?

....

[1]

e) Explain why cutting the magnesium into smaller pieces affects the rate of this reaction.

....

....

[2]

f) State **one** change that could be made to alter the rate of the reaction, other than changing the concentration and the size of the magnesium pieces.

....

[1]

[Total 10 marks]

Score:

18

Catalysts

1 Which of the following statements about catalysts is correct? **Grade 4-6**

▢ **A** Catalysts are very reactive, so only small amounts of catalyst are required during reactions.

▢ **B** The products formed during a reaction depend on whether or not a catalyst is used.

▢ **C** Most catalysts need to be added to the reaction mixture in excess.

▢ **D** As catalysts are not used up during chemical reactions, only small amounts are required.

[Total 1 mark]

2 A student carries out a reaction between hydrogen gas and iodine gas to form hydrogen iodide (HI). **Grade 6-7**

a) When cerium oxide is mixed with the hydrogen and iodine gases, the rate of reaction increases.

  i) What does this suggest about cerium oxide?

  ....

[1]

  ii) Explain how cerium oxide increases the rate of the reaction.

  ....

  ....

[2]

b) State whether the reaction equation will change if cerium oxide is present in the reaction vessel. Explain your answer.

  ....

  ....

[2]

c) Sketch and label **two** reaction profiles on the axes below to show the difference between the reaction of hydrogen and iodine with and without cerium oxide. The energy of the products is lower than the energy of the reactants.

Energy

Progress of Reaction

[2]

[Total 7 marks]

Score: ▢

8

Paper 2

Measuring Rates of Reaction

1 Hydrogen peroxide decomposes into water and oxygen. *(Grade 3-4)*

Which method would be appropriate for measuring the rate of this reaction?

☐ **A** Measuring the volume of gas produced at regular intervals.

☐ **B** Measuring the temperature.

☐ **C** Timing how long the reaction takes to go cloudy.

☐ **D** Weighing the amount of water produced.

[Total 1 mark]

2 The rate of a reaction can be measured using different methods. *(Grade 6-7)*

a) If one of the products is a gas, the rate of reaction can be measured by recording the change in mass of the reaction vessel using a mass balance.

   i) Suggest **one** disadvantage of this method.

   ....

   ....

   [1]

   ii) Describe a method, other than measuring a change in mass, that could be used to measure the rate of a reaction when one of the products is a gas.

   ....

   ....

   [1]

b) i) Briefly describe how you could measure the rate of a reaction that produces a precipitate.

   ....

   ....

   ....

   [2]

   ii) A student is investigating how the concentration of a reactant affects the rate of a reaction that produces a precipitate. She carries out the reaction with different concentrations of reactant and measures the rate of reaction for each concentration.
   What is the dependent variable in this method?

   ....

   [1]

   [Total 5 marks]

Score: ☐

6

Rate of Reaction Experiments

1 Oxygen and water can be produced by the decomposition of hydrogen peroxide (H_2O_2). **PRACTICAL**

a) Complete this balanced symbol equation for the decomposition of hydrogen peroxide, including state symbols.

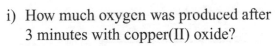

..............$H_2O_{2\,(aq)} \rightarrow$ .... (............) + $O_{2\,(............)}$

[2]

b) Samples of three catalysts with the same surface area were added to hydrogen peroxide solution. The same volume and concentration of hydrogen peroxide was used each time. The volume of oxygen produced over time was measured and recorded, and is shown in the graph.

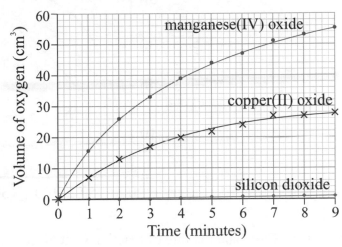

i) How much oxygen was produced after 3 minutes with copper(II) oxide?

Volume of oxygen = ... cm³

[1]

ii) State, with a reason, the most effective catalyst.

Most effective catalyst ....

Reason ....

....

[2]

[Total 5 marks]

2 A scientist is investigating how the quantity of reactants affects the rate of the reaction between hydrochloric acid (HCl) with marble chips. He carried out two reactions, **X** and **Y**. Reaction **X** used 0.500 g of marble chips and an excess of 0.100 mol/dm³ HCl.

Using the graph on the right, determine which of the following sets of conditions could have resulted in reaction **Y**.

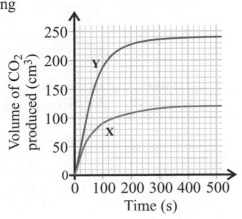

☐ **A** 0.250 g of marble chips and an excess of 0.100 mol/dm³ hydrochloric acid.

☐ **B** 1.00 g of marble chips and an excess of 0.100 mol/dm³ hydrochloric acid.

☐ **C** 0.250 g of marble chips and an excess of 0.200 mol/dm³ hydrochloric acid.

☐ **D** 1.00 g of marble chips and an excess of 0.200 mol/dm³ hydrochloric acid.

[Total 1 mark]

3 A student wanted to calculate the rate of reaction between nitric acid and zinc. He carried out two experiments under the same conditions, but in one he used zinc ribbons and in the other he used zinc powder.

The graph below shows the rate of reaction for both experiments, labelled **Q** and **R**.

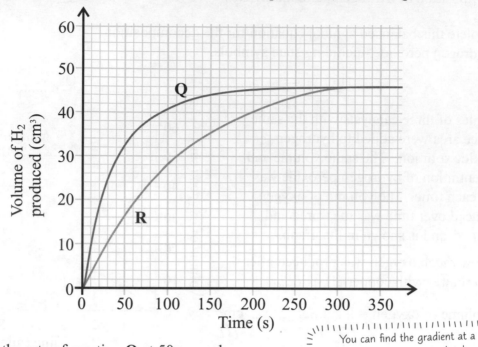

a) i) Calculate the rate of reaction **Q** at 50 seconds.

> You can find the gradient at a particular point on a curve by drawing a tangent to the curve at that point.

rate = ... cm³/s

[3]

ii) Calculate the rate of reaction **R** at 120 seconds.

rate = ... cm³/s

[3]

b) State which reaction, **Q** or **R**, used the powdered zinc. Explain your answer.

....

....

....

[3]

c) State **one** variable that the student would have controlled in order to make the experiment scientifically valid. Explain why this variable needed to be controlled.

....

....

[2]

[Total 11 marks]

Score: ☐

17

Section 5 — Physical Chemistry

Reversible Reactions

1   In the reaction below, substances A and B react to form substances C and D.

$$2A_{(g)} + B_{(g)} \rightleftharpoons 2C_{(g)} + D_{(g)}$$

a) What can you deduce about this reaction from the symbol $\rightleftharpoons$?

....

[1]

b) What is meant by the term **dynamic equilibrium**?

....

....

[1]

c) In the above reaction, the forward reaction is exothermic.

i) Does the reverse reaction take in or give out energy? Explain your answer.

....

....

[2]

ii) Explain why changing the temperature of a reversible reaction can affect the position of the equilibrium.

....

....

[2]

iii) If the temperature of the above reaction is raised, will the equilibrium position move to the right or to the left?

....

[1]

d) State and explain the effect of changing the pressure on the position of equilibrium in the above reaction.

....

....

[2]

e) Ammonium chloride is heated in a beaker inside a fume cupboard to form ammonia gas and hydrogen chloride gas. Why can this reaction not reach equilibrium even though it is reversible?

....

....

[1]

[Total 10 marks]

2 When blue hydrated copper(II) sulfate is heated, steam and anhydrous white copper(II) sulfate are produced.

$$CuSO_4.5H_2O_{(s)} \rightleftharpoons CuSO_{4(s)} + 5H_2O_{(g)}$$

a) From the information given in the question, state whether the forward reaction is exothermic or endothermic. Give a reason for your answer.

....

....

[2]

b) A student has a beaker containing some anhydrous copper(II) sulfate powder. A few drops of water are added to the beaker from a pipette. Two changes are observed in the beaker.

i) Describe what happens to the colour of the copper(II) sulfate.

....

[1]

ii) What happens to the temperature of the mixture in the beaker?

....

[1]

[Total 4 marks]

3 When ammonium nitrate is heated, it breaks down into ammonia and hydrogen chloride. The reaction is reversible. (Grade 7-9)

$$NH_4Cl_{(s)} \rightleftharpoons NH_{3(g)} + HCl_{(g)}$$

Two students are trying to deduce the optimum conditions to favour the forward reaction.

The first student suggests a temperature of 375 °C and a pressure of 1 atmosphere.
The second student suggests a temperature of 250 °C and a pressure of 5 atmospheres.

Using your knowledge of equilibrium reactions, deduce which conditions are more favourable for the forward reaction. Explain your answer.

....

....

....

....

....

....

....

[Total 5 marks]

Score:

19

Section 5 — Physical Chemistry

Organic Compounds

1 Which of the following is a structural formula?

☐ **A** C_nH_{2n} ☐ **B** $CH_3CH_2CH_3$ ☐ **C** CH   ☐ **D** C_2H_4

[Total 1 mark]

2 Three of the following structures belong to the same homologous series. Identify the structure that belongs to a **different** homologous series.

☐ **A**

$$H-\overset{\displaystyle H}{\underset{\displaystyle H}{C}}-\overset{\displaystyle H}{\underset{\displaystyle H}{C}}-C\overset{\displaystyle O}{\underset{\displaystyle O-H}{}}$$

☐ **C**

$$H-\overset{\displaystyle H}{\underset{\displaystyle H}{C}}-\overset{\displaystyle H}{\underset{\displaystyle H}{C}}-O-H$$

☐ **B**

$$H-\overset{\displaystyle H}{C}-H$$
$$\underset{\displaystyle O}{\big|}$$
$$\underset{\displaystyle H}{\big|}$$

☐ **D**

$$H-\overset{\displaystyle H}{\underset{\displaystyle H}{C}}-\overset{\displaystyle O}{\underset{\displaystyle H}{C}}-\overset{\displaystyle H}{\underset{\displaystyle H}{C}}-H$$

[Total 1 mark]

3 Alkenes are a homologous series of hydrocarbons.

a) Describe what is meant by the term **homologous series**.

....

[1]

b) The structure of an alkene is shown below.

$$H-\overset{\displaystyle H}{\underset{\displaystyle H}{C}}-\overset{\displaystyle H}{C}=\overset{\displaystyle H}{C}-\overset{\displaystyle H}{\underset{\displaystyle H}{C}}-\overset{\displaystyle H}{\underset{\displaystyle H}{C}}-H$$

i) Circle the functional group in the alkene.

[1]

ii) Name this alkene. ....

[1]

iii) Write the empirical formula of this alkene. ....

[1]

[Total 4 marks]

4 Draw the displayed formula of a molecule of hexane.

[Total 1 mark]

5 Draw the displayed formula of the molecule with the structural formula $CH_3CH_2C(=O)OCH_3$.

[Total 1 mark]

6 A student carries out the reaction between ethanol and a carboxylic acid, **A**. The displayed formula of carboxylic acid **A** is shown below.

A

a) Name carboxylic acid **A**.

....

[1]

b) The student carries out the reaction again, but uses a different carboxylic acid, **B**. Will carboxylic acid **B** react in the same way as carboxylic acid **A**? Explain your answer.

....

....

[1]

[Total 2 marks]

Score:

10

Section 6 — Organic Chemistry

Isomers

1   Which of the following molecules is **not** an isomer of the other three?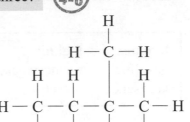

☐ **A**

☐ **B**

☐ **C**

☐ **D**

[Total 1 mark]

2   The displayed formula of a molecule is shown below.   (Grade 6-7)

$$Br - C - C - C - H$$

a)   Draw the displayed formula of an isomer of the molecule shown above.

[1]

b)   The molecular formula of a straight chain molecule is C_4H_9Cl.
   Draw the displayed formula of **both** isomers of this molecule.

[2]

[Total 3 marks]

Exam Practice Tip

Isomerism can be pretty tough to get your head around. There are plenty of ways to rearrange atoms in a molecule, and you need to be able to spot the different forms — watch out for clues such as two molecules having differently shaped carbon chains, or the same functional group appearing in different places.

Score

4

Section 6 — Organic Chemistry

Crude Oil

1 Label the fractionating column below with the names of the fractions shown in the box.

bitumen	fuel oil
gasoline	refinery gases
kerosene	diesel

crude → oil

....

....

....

....

....

....

[Total 3 marks]

2 Heptane and triacontane are two molecules that are present in two of the fractions produced by the fractional distillation of crude oil.

The table below shows the boiling points of these two molecules.

Hydrocarbon	Chemical formula	Boiling point (°C)
Heptane	C_7H_{16}	98
Triacontane	$C_{30}H_{62}$	450

a) Triacontane is present in the fuel oil fraction. Give **two** uses of fuel oil.

1 ....

2 ....

[2]

b) Which of these two hydrocarbons would you expect to be collected **further down** the fractionating column?
Explain your answer, with reference to the boiling points of the hydrocarbons.

....

....

....

....

[3]

[Total 5 marks]

Score:

8

Section 6 — Organic Chemistry

Cracking

1 When decane is cracked, octane and ethene can be produced.

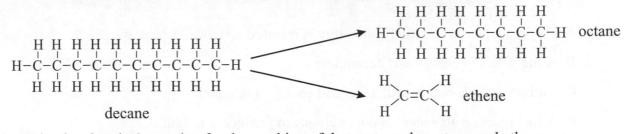

a) Write the chemical equation for the cracking of decane to make octane and ethene.

....
[1]

b) Which statement best describes the differences in the physical properties of octane and decane?

☐ **A** Octane has a lower boiling point and a higher viscocity than decane.

☐ **B** Octane has a higher boiling point and a higher viscocity than decane.

☐ **C** Octane has a higher boiling point and a lower viscocity than decane.

☐ **D** Octane has a lower boiling point and a lower viscocity than decane.

[1]

[Total 2 marks]

2 Cracking alters the molecules obtained in fractional distillation.

a) The apparatus shown on the right can be used to crack kerosene in the lab.

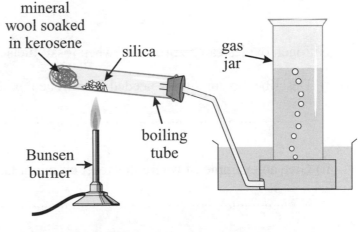

i) Suggest the role of the silica.

....
[1]

ii) The alkanes produced by cracking collect in the boiling tube. Suggest what collects in the gas jar.

....
[1]

b) Why is cracking necessary? Discuss both types of hydrocarbon produced.

....

....

....

....
[4]

[Total 6 marks]

Score: ☐

8

Burning Hydrocarbons

1 Which of the following statements best describes what occurs during a combustion reaction? *(Grade 3-4)*

☐ **A** Oxygen reacts with a fuel and energy is released.

☐ **B** A fuel takes in energy and decomposes.

☐ **C** Carbon dioxide reacts with a fuel and energy is released.

☐ **D** A fuel reacts with water vapour in clouds to produce acid rain.

[Total 1 mark]

2 Fumes from faulty central heating boilers can contain carbon monoxide. *(Grade 4-6)*

a) What can cause carbon monoxide to be produced when fuel is burnt in a boiler?

....

[1]

b) Describe the effect that carbon monoxide has on the human body.

....

....

[1]

[Total 2 marks]

3 Nitrogen oxides can be produced when fossil fuels are burnt. *(Grade 4-6)*

a) i) Describe the conditions needed for nitrogen oxides to form.

....

[1]

ii) Give an example of where this reaction might take place.

....

[1]

b) Nitrogen oxides react with water vapour in the atmosphere.
   Name the product that is formed when this occurs.

....

[1]

c) Nitrogen oxides contribute to acid rain.
   Name **one** other gas that contributes to acid rain.

....

[1]

[Total 4 marks]

4 Hydrocarbons can be used as fuels by burning them in oxygen. *Grade 6-7*

a) Which of the following compounds is **not** produced when a hydrocarbon is burned in an insufficient amount of oxygen?

☐ **A** H_2O

☐ **B** CO

☐ **C** NH_3

☐ **D** CO_2

[1]

b) Write a word equation for the complete combustion of propane, C_3H_8.

....

[1]

c) Dodecene is a hydrocarbon with the molecular formula $C_{12}H_{24}$.

i) Write a balanced symbol equation for the complete combustion of dodecene.

....

[2]

ii) Under certain conditions, combustion of dodecene can produce a solid made of particles of impure carbon. Name this solid.

....

[1]

[Total 5 marks]

5 A student burns a small amount of an unknown hydrocarbon, **A**, in the lab. An incomplete symbol equation for the reaction is shown below. *Grade 7-9*

$$A \ + \ O_2 \ \rightarrow \ 9CO_2 \ + \ 10H_2O$$

a) Use the symbol equation for the reaction to deduce the molecular formula of hydrocarbon **A**.

....

[1]

b) The student uses a Bunsen burner to burn a sample of a fuel, **B**, and collects some of the gas produced in a test tube containing a piece of damp litmus paper. The litmus paper turns red, indicating that an acid is present.

Suggest an impurity that might be present in fuel **B**.

....

[1]

[Total 2 marks]

Score: ☐

14

 ☐ ☐ ☐

Section 6 — Organic Chemistry

Alkanes

1 Which of the following structural formulae belongs to an alkane? *Grade 4-6*

- [ ] **A** CH_2CH_2
- [ ] **B** $CH_3CH_2CHCHCH_3$
- [ ] **C** $CH_3CH_2CH_2CH_2CH_3$
- [ ] **D** $CH_3CH_2CH_2OH$

[Total 1 mark]

2 Alkanes are a group of saturated hydrocarbon compounds. *Grade 6-7*

a) State the general formula of the alkane homologous series.

....

[1]

b) i) Name the alkane that contains **two** carbon atoms.

....

[1]

ii) State the number of hydrogen atoms that this alkane contains.

....

[1]

> Alkanes all have the same general formula, so as long as you know the number of carbon atoms in an alkane, you don't need to remember how many hydrogens it contains — you can work that out from the number of carbons.

c) Draw the displayed formula of butane.

[1]

d) Methane will react with bromine in the presence of UV light.

i) Complete the word equation for this reaction.

methane + bromine $\xrightarrow{\text{UV}}$ .... + ...

[2]

ii) Name the type of reaction shown in part i).

....

[1]

[Total 7 marks]

Score:

8

Alkenes

1 Alkenes are a group of unsaturated hydrocarbon molecules.

a) State the general formula of the alkenes. ....

[1]

b) Define the term **unsaturated**.

....

[1]

[Total 2 marks]

2 Alkenes can react reaction with halogens. An example of the reactants that can take part in this type of reaction is shown below.

$$H_2C - CH = CH - CH_3 \ + \ Br_2 \longrightarrow X$$

Draw the displayed formula of product **X**.

[Total 1 mark]

3 A student investigated the reactivity of some hydrocarbons.

a) The student added a sample of a hydrocarbon, **A**, to bromine water. A reaction took place.

i) The molecular formula of the product formed was $C_3H_6Br_2$.

Write the structural formula of hydrocarbon **A**. ....

[1]

ii) What would the student expect to observe when hydrocarbon **A** was added to bromine water?

....

[1]

iii) Name the type of reaction that took place between the hydrocarbon and the bromine water.

....

[1]

b) The student took some bromine water and added it to a hydrocarbon with the chemical formula, C_2H_6. What would you expect the student to have observed? Explain your answer.

....

....

[3]

[Total 6 marks]

Score:

9

Section 6 — Organic Chemistry

Alcohols

1 Alcohols are a series of organic compounds with a wide range of industrial applications.

a) An alcohol containing 3 carbons is commonly used as a solvent.
   What is the name given to this alcohol?

   ....
                                                                                                                              [1]

b) Ethanol is present in alcoholic drinks. Give the structural formula for ethanol.

   ....
                                                                                                                              [1]

c) Methanol can be used as an additive to fuels to improve combustion.
   Draw the displayed formula for methanol.

                                                                                                                              [1]
                                                                                                                   [Total 3 marks]

2 Two organic molecules, **Y** and **Z**, were added to separate test tubes containing
   acidified potassium dichromate(VI). Only one of the organic molecules reacted.

a) The two possible organic molecules are shown below.
   Identify which molecule, **Y** or **Z**, reacted. Explain your answer.

```
Y      H   H   H   H                    Z      H   H   H   H
       |   |   |   |                            |   |   |   |
   H — C — C — C — C — O — H              H — C — C — C — C — H
       |   |   |   |                            |   |   |   |
       H   H   H   H                            H   H   H   H
```

   ....

   ....

   ....

   ....
                                                                                                                              [4]

b) Draw the displayed formula of the organic product that was formed in the reaction.

                                                                                                                              [1]
                                                                                                                   [Total 5 marks]

Score:

8

Production of Ethanol

1 Yeast can be used to convert sugars into ethanol. What is the name given to this process? *(Grade 3-4)*

☐ **A** extraction   ☐ **C** denaturing

☐ **B** fermentation   ☐ **D** distillation

[Total 1 mark]

2 Two different methods can be used to manufacture ethanol. The incomplete table below shows some information about the two methods. *(Grade 6-7)*

a) Complete the table.

Method	Reaction	Temperature needed
A	$C_2H_4 + \text{.....................} \rightarrow C_2H_5OH$	....
B	$C_6H_{12}O_6 \rightarrow 2CO_2 + \text{..........}C_2H_5OH$	....

[4]

b) Method **A** requires a high temperature.
State the pressure and type of catalyst that are typically used in the reaction.

Pressure ....

Catalyst ....

[2]

c) Method **B** should be carried out in an environment without oxygen.

i) Predict the pH of the solution that would form if method **B** was carried out in a flask that was open to the air. Explain your answer.

....

....

[2]

ii) A scientist attempted to use method **B** to produce ethanol at 250 °C.
After 24 hours, no product had been formed. Explain why.

....

....

[2]

[Total 10 marks]

Score

☐

11

Paper 2

 ☐ ☐ ☐

Section 6 — Organic Chemistry

Carboxylic Acids

Paper 2

1 Methanoic acid is the simplest carboxylic acid possible. **Grade 4-6**

a) What is the functional group in methanoic acid?

☐ **A** $-CH_3$ ☐ **B** C=C   ☐ **C** $-OH$ ☐ **D** $-COOH$

[1]

b) Write the structural formula of methanoic acid.

....

[1]

c) Methanoic acid reacts with potassium. What gas is produced?

....

[1]

[Total 3 marks]

2 A student reacts a small sample of a carboxylic acid, **A**, with potassium carbonate. **Grade 6-7**

a) The structural formula of carboxylic acid **A** is $CH_3CH_2CH_2COOH$.

i) Name carboxylic acid **A**. ....

[1]

ii) Draw the displayed formula of carboxylic acid **A**.

[1]

b) A salt is produced in the reaction of carboxylic acid **A** with potassium carbonate.

Name the other **two** products of this reaction.

1 ....

2 ....

[2]

c) The student has an aqueous solution of a second carboxylic acid, **B**. She opens the bottle and notices a strong smell of vinegar. Suggest the identity of carboxylic acid **B**.

....

[1]

[Total 5 marks]

Score: ☐

8

Esters

1 Esters are volatile compounds that are often used in perfumes.

a) Explain what is meant by the term **volatile**.

....
[1]

b) Apart from volatility, give **one** other property of esters that makes them suitable for use in perfumes.

....
[1]

c) Other than perfumes, give **one** use of esters in the chemical industry.

....
[1]

[Total 3 marks]

2 When ethanol is heated with ethanoic acid in the presence of a catalyst, an ester is produced.

a) Name a catalyst that could be used for this reaction.

....
[1]

b) Complete the chemical equation for this reaction.

CH_3COOH + ... → .... + H_2O
[1]

c) Name the ester produced in this reaction.

....
[1]

d) State the functional group of the esters.

....
[1]

[Total 4 marks]

3 Draw the displayed formulae of the carboxylic acid and the alcohol that can be reacted together to produce propyl methanoate.

[Total 2 marks]

4 Some students want to carry out a reaction to produce an ester.
Esters are produced when alcohols are heated with carboxylic acids. (Grade 7-9) PRACTICAL

a) Their teacher reminds them that alcohols and esters are both flammable
and should not be heated over an open flame.
Suggest a method that the students could use to heat the reaction mixture safely.

....

....

[1]

b) The students start by adding a small amount of concentrated sulfuric acid to a boiling tube.

i) State the purpose of the sulfuric acid in this reaction.

....

[1]

ii) Concentrated sulfuric acid is hazardous as it can burn the skin.
Suggest **two** ways in which the students could reduce the risk associated with this hazard.

1 ....

2 ....

[2]

c) The students add equal volumes of propanoic acid and methanol to the boiling tube,
and begin to heat the mixture. Draw the displayed formula of the ester that students
would expect to produce during the reaction.

[1]

d) Suggest how the students could quickly tell if the reaction has been successful.

....

[1]

e) The students decide to carry out another reaction to make the ester butyl propanoate.
State which carboxylic acid and alcohol they should use to make butyl propanoate.

Carboxylic acid ....

Alcohol ....

[2]

[Total 8 marks]

Exam Practice Tip

Naming esters can be tricky. Remember, the first part of the name comes from the alcohol, and the second
part comes from the carboxylic acid. So for example, if you reacted ethanol with pentanoic acid, the ester
formed would be called ethyl pentanoate. Make sure to double check your answer, it's easy to get muddled up.

Score

[ ]
────
17

Addition Polymers

1 Polymers can be formed in addition polymerisation reactions.

a) Which of these homologous series can form addition polymers?

☐ **A** alkenes and alkanes

☐ **B** alkenes only

☐ **C** haloalkanes only

☐ **D** alkanes and haloalkanes

[1]

b) The equation below shows a polymerisation reaction to form poly(ethene).

i) What is the name of the monomer used to form poly(ethene)?

....

[1]

ii) Give the functional group involved in this reaction.

....

[1]

[Total 3 marks]

2 The polymer poly(propene) can be made by addition polymerisation.

The diagram below shows the displayed formula for part of a poly(propene) molecule.

$$-\underset{\underset{H}{|}}{\overset{\overset{H}{|}}{C}}-\underset{\underset{CH_3}{|}}{\overset{\overset{H}{|}}{C}}-\underset{\underset{H}{|}}{\overset{\overset{H}{|}}{C}}-\underset{\underset{CH_3}{|}}{\overset{\overset{H}{|}}{C}}-\underset{\underset{H}{|}}{\overset{\overset{H}{|}}{C}}-\underset{\underset{CH_3}{|}}{\overset{\overset{H}{|}}{C}}-\underset{\underset{H}{|}}{\overset{\overset{H}{|}}{C}}-\underset{\underset{CH_3}{|}}{\overset{\overset{H}{|}}{C}}-$$

a) i) Draw the structure of the repeat unit of poly(propene).

[1]

ii) Draw the structure of the monomer that is used to make poly(propene).

[1]

iii) Give the name of the monomer used to make poly(propene).

....

[1]

b) The repeat unit of a different polymer is shown below.

$$\left(\begin{array}{cc} Cl & H \\ | & | \\ C - C \\ | & | \\ H & H \end{array}\right)_n$$

Name the polymer formed from this repeat unit.

....

[1]

c) Most addition polymers are difficult to dispose of, so it's good for the environment to reuse them as many times as possible. Explain why addition polymers are difficult to dispose of.

....

....

[2]

[Total 6 marks]

3   Vinyl acetate polymerises to form polyvinyl acetate. The formula of vinyl acetate is shown on the right. **(Grade 6-7)**

Draw the displayed formula of the repeat unit of polyvinyl acetate.

[Total 1 mark]

4   The structural formula of the monomer that makes up poly(tetrafluoroethene) (PTFE) is CF_2CF_2. **(Grade 7-9)**

Draw the displayed formula of the repeat unit of PTFE.

[Total 1 mark]

Exam Practice Tip	Score
The monomers of addition polymers must have a C=C bond, but in polymer form this double bond becomes a single bond. Carbon always has four bonds, so if you're drawing the repeat unit of a polymer, count how many bonds the carbon atoms have. This way, you can check the bonds to make sure they're all present and correct.	☐ —— **11**

Polyesters

1   Which of these molecules **cannot** take part in condensation polymerisation reactions?

☐ **A**   HO—C—C—C—C—C—C—C<O\OH (with H atoms on each carbon)

☐ **C**   O=C(HO)—C(H)(H)—C=O(OH)

☐ **B**   HO—C—C—C—C—C—C—OH (with H atoms on each carbon)

☐ **D**   H—C(H)(H)—C(H)=C(H)—C(H)(H)—H

[Total 1 mark]

2   A condensation polymerisation reaction between butanedioic acid and ethanediol produces a polyester, **D**, and another product, **E**.

O=C(HO)—C(H)(H)—C(H)(H)—C=O(OH)   +   HO—C(H)(H)—C(H)(H)—OH   →   **D**   +   **E**

a)   i)   Draw the displayed formula of the repeat unit of polyester **D**.

[2]

     ii)   What is the formula of the product, **E**?

....

[1]

b)   In a different polymerisation reaction, pentanedioic acid, $HOOC(CH_2)_3COOH$, reacts with propanediol, $HO(CH_2)_3OH$. A polyester, **F**, is formed. Draw the repeat unit of **F**.

[2]

[Total 5 marks]

Score: ☐

6

Edexcel International GCSE

Chemistry

Paper 1C

Practice Paper
Time allowed: 2 hours

Total marks:

You must have:
* A ruler.
* A calculator.

Instructions to candidates
* Use **black** ink to write your answers.
* Write your name and other details in the spaces provided above.
* Answer **all** questions in the spaces provided.
* In calculations, show clearly how you worked out your answers.
* You will need to answer some questions by placing a cross in a box, like this: ☒
  To change your answer, draw a line through the box like this: ☒
  Then mark your new answer as normal.

Information for candidates
* The marks available are given in brackets at the end of each question.
* There are 110 marks available for this paper.

Advice for candidates
* Read all the questions carefully.
* Write your answers as clearly and neatly as possible.
* Keep in mind how much time you have left.

Answer **all** questions

1   Atoms contain protons, neutrons and electrons.

(a)   The diagram below shows the structure of an atom.
       Label a proton.

[1]

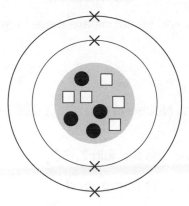

(b)   The table below shows the numbers of protons, neutrons and electrons in
       six different atoms.

Atom	Number of protons	Number of neutrons	Number of electrons
A	5	6	5
B	7	7	7
C	6	8	6
D	6	6	6
E	10	10	10
F	4	5	4

Which **two** atoms are isotopes of the same element? Explain your answer.

Atoms .... and ....

Explanation ....

....

....

[2]

Zinc appears in the periodic table as shown below.

65
Zn
Zinc
30

(c) How many protons, neutrons and electrons are there in an atom of zinc?

Protons .... Neutrons .... Electrons ....

[3]

(d) Zinc sulfate is a compound with the formula $ZnSO_4$.

(i) Describe what is meant by the term **compound**.

....

....

[2]

(ii) Calculate the relative formula mass of zinc sulfate.

Relative formula mass = ...

[2]

[Total 10 marks]

2 Nitrogen dioxide is an atmospheric pollutant.

(a) Suggest why nitrogen dioxide levels can be particularly high in cities.

....

....

....

....

[2]

(b) Nitrogen dioxide can react with water in the atmosphere to form nitric acid, which falls as acid rain. Acid rain can damage buildings made from limestone, which is mainly calcium carbonate.

(i) Complete the word equation for the reaction between nitric acid and calcium carbonate.

nitric acid + calcium carbonate →

.... + ... + ...

[2]

(ii) Name **one** other gas that can cause acid rain.

....

[1]

(c) Nitrogen dioxide is a covalent compound with a boiling point of 21 °C.
Explain, in terms of its structure and bonding, why nitrogen dioxide
has such a low boiling point.

....

....

....

....

....

[3]

[Total 8 marks]

Turn over ▶

3   The halogens make up Group 7 of the periodic table.
     The table below shows some of the physical properties of the first four halogens.

Halogen	Atomic number	Melting Point (°C)	Boiling Point (°C)	Colour at room temperature
Fluorine	9	−220	−188	very pale yellow
Chlorine	17		−34	green
Bromine	35	−7	59	
Iodine	53	114	185	dark grey

(a) (i)   Predict the melting point of chlorine, using the data in the table.

    ☐ **A**   −231 °C

    ☐ **B**   −216 °C

    ☐ **C**   −101 °C

    ☐ **D**   107 °C

[1]

(ii) Explain your answer to part i).

....

....

[1]

(b)   Describe the appearance of bromine at room temperature.

....

[2]

(c)   Write down the balanced symbol equation for the reaction between bromine and potassium iodide.

....

[2]

(d) (i) Complete the diagram below to show the electronic structure of a chlorine atom. Mark each electron using an 'X'.

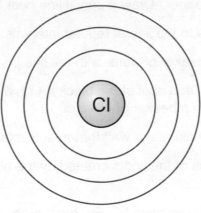

[1]

(ii) Explain how the group number of chlorine in the periodic table is related to its electronic structure.

....

....

....

[2]

(e) Chlorine is bubbled through sodium iodide solution. What will happen?
Explain your answer in terms of the relative positions of chlorine and iodine in the periodic table.

....

....

....

....

....

[3]

(f) Chlorine can combine with hydrogen to form hydrogen chloride.
Explain why hydrogen chloride forms an acidic solution in water.

....

....

....

[2]

[Total 14 marks]

Turn over ▶

Practice Paper 1C

4 A student wanted to find out which of five dyes could be present in a particular black ink.

(a) The student was asked to suggest a method. This is the method the student suggested:

- Take a piece of filter paper. Draw a pencil line near the bottom.

- Add spots of the dyes to the line at regular intervals.

- Put the paper into a beaker of water with the line just touching the water.

- Repeat these steps with a spot of the black ink on a second piece of filter paper, and put this paper into a beaker of ethanol.

- Place a lid on each beaker, and wait for the solvents to travel to the top of the paper.

- Compare the positions of the spots created by the black ink with those created by the dyes.

Identify **two** problems with this method. For each problem, suggest how you would alter the method to carry out the experiment correctly.

You can assume the student takes sensible safety precautions.

Problem 1 ....

....

....

Correction ....

....

....

....

Problem 2 ....

....

....

Correction ....

....

....

....

[4]

(b)   The student repeated the experiment using the correct method.
        The results are shown below.

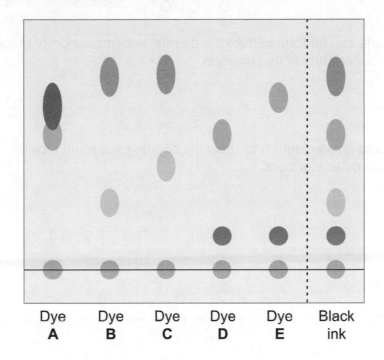

Diagram not to scale.

        Dye   Dye   Dye   Dye   Dye   Black
         A   B   C   D   E   ink

Which dyes (**A-E**) could have been present in the black ink? Explain your answer.

Dyes ....

Explanation ....

....

....

....

                                                                                                              [2]

(c)   The student measured the distances moved by the solvent and one of the spots in the
        black ink. She found that the solvent had moved 6.4 cm from the baseline, and that the
        spot had moved 4.8 cm.
        Calculate the R_f value of the spot in the black ink.

R_f value = ...

                                                                                                              [1]

                                                                                           [Total 7 marks]

5   Carbon dioxide is a simple molecule whose displayed formula is shown below.

$$O=C=O$$

(a)   Carbon dioxide can be formed from the thermal decomposition of magnesium carbonate. Name the other product of this reaction.

....

                                               [1]

(b)   Draw a dot and cross diagram to show the bonding in carbon dioxide. Only show the outer electrons.

[2]

(c)   The molecular formula of magnesium carbonate is $MgCO_3$. Calculate the percentage mass of carbon in magnesium carbonate.

mass of carbon = ... %

[2]

(d)   Carbon dioxide is a greenhouse gas.

   (i)   Explain what is meant by the term **greenhouse gas**.

   ....

   ....

   ....

                                                                                                    [2]

   (ii) State the percentage of the air that is made up of carbon dioxide.

   ....

                                                                                                    [1]

   (iii) Give **one** possible effect of increasing the amount of carbon dioxide in the atmosphere.

   ....

   ....

                                                                                                    [1]
                                                                                      [Total 9 marks]

6   Analytical tests can be used to identify different substances.

(a) (i)   A test is carried out to distinguish between a solution of iron(II) chloride
and a solution of iron(III) chloride.

Describe the test and the result expected for each solution.

....

....

....

....

....

[2]

(ii)   Another test is carried out to distinguish between a solution of sodium chloride
and a solution of sodium iodide.

Describe the test and the result expected for each solution.

....

....

....

....

....

[2]

(b)   When an unknown compound is placed in a blue Bunsen flame, it gives a yellow colour.
If dilute acid is added to the compound, a gas is produced. When this gas is bubbled
through limewater, the limewater goes cloudy.

Identify the compound by its chemical name.

....

[2]

[Total 6 marks]

7 A student reacts four different metals with dilute sulfuric acid.
She controls all of the relevant variables to make sure that the test is fair.
She collects the gas given off by each reaction in a gas syringe.
The diagrams below show all four reactions after 30 seconds.

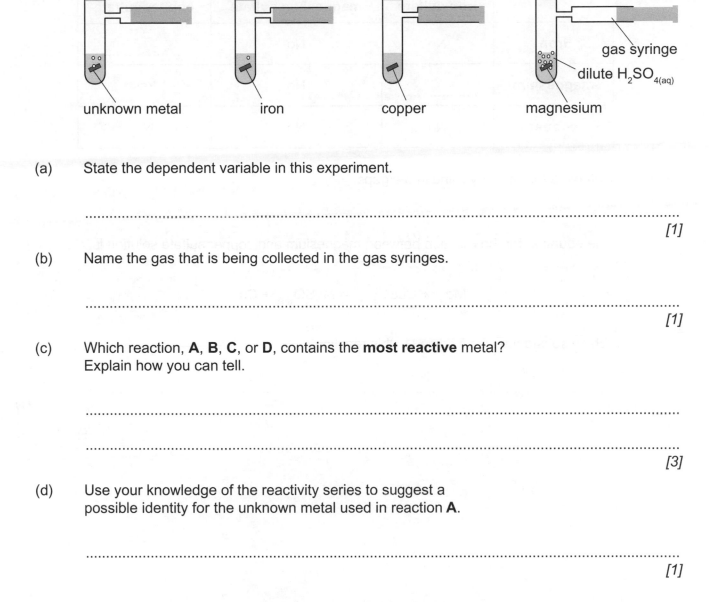

Reaction A — unknown metal
Reaction B — iron
Reaction C — copper
Reaction D — magnesium, gas syringe, dilute $H_2SO_{4(aq)}$

(a) State the dependent variable in this experiment.

....
[1]

(b) Name the gas that is being collected in the gas syringes.

....
[1]

(c) Which reaction, **A**, **B**, **C**, or **D**, contains the **most reactive** metal?
Explain how you can tell.

....

....
[3]

(d) Use your knowledge of the reactivity series to suggest a
possible identity for the unknown metal used in reaction **A**.

....
[1]

Turn over ▶

(e)   In another experiment, the student placed pieces of different metals in metal salt solutions. She left them for 10 minutes. The student then recorded whether any reaction had occurred. The results of this experiment are shown in the table below.

	Did any reaction occur with:		
	iron sulfate	magnesium sulfate	copper sulfate
iron	No	No	....
magnesium	....	No	Yes
copper	No	No	No

Complete the table by filling in the gaps.

[2]

(f)   The equation for the reaction between magnesium and copper sulfate solution is:

$$Mg_{(s)} + CuSO_{4(aq)} \rightarrow MgSO_{4(aq)} + Cu_{(s)}$$

Which substance was oxidised in this reaction?

....

[1]

[Total 9 marks]

8 The displayed formulae of two gases are shown below.

Gas **A** $H-\overset{\displaystyle H}{\underset{\displaystyle H}{C}}-\overset{\displaystyle H}{\underset{\displaystyle H}{C}}-\overset{\displaystyle H}{\underset{\displaystyle H}{C}}-H$

Gas **B** $H-\overset{\displaystyle H}{\underset{\displaystyle H}{C}}-\overset{\displaystyle H}{C}=C\overset{\displaystyle H}{\underset{\displaystyle H}{}}$

(a) Name gas **B**.

....

[1]

(b) State the name given to unsaturated hydrocarbons like gas **B**.

....

[1]

(c) Pentane is a saturated compound. Draw the displayed formula of pentane.

[1]

(d) Describe a test that you could use to distinguish between gas **A** and gas **B**.
State what you would observe in each case.

Test: ....

Observations:

Gas **A**: ....

Gas **B**: ....

[2]

(e) In terms of bond breaking and bond formation, explain the observation for gas **B**.

....

....

....

[2]

Turn over ▶

(f)   Gas **A** is burnt in a plentiful supply of oxygen.
Write a balanced chemical equation for this reaction.

....

[2]

(g)   Demand for short chain hydrocarbons, such as gas **A** and gas **B,** is much higher than for longer chain hydrocarbons.

(i)   Name the process by which long chain hydrocarbons are split into short chain hydrocarbons.

....

[1]

(ii)   Decane, $C_{10}H_{22}$, can be split using the process in (i) into gas **B** and heptane, C_7H_{16}.
Write these three hydrocarbons in order of increasing viscosity.

....

[1]

[Total 11 marks]

9 Self-heating cans use exothermic chemical reactions to heat up their contents.
When a seal is broken two chemicals mix and react, heating up the can.
Calcium oxide and water can be used to heat up drinks in this way.

(a) Explain what is meant by an **exothermic reaction**.

....

....
[1]

(b) A student wanted to test the reaction of different substances with water
to see if they could be used to cool drinks down.

Outline an experiment the student could carry out to test different substances.

....

....

....

....

....
[3]

(c) Calcium oxide (CaO) is produced when iron(III) oxide (Fe_2O_3) reacts with calcium.
Iron is also produced. Write a balanced chemical equation for this reaction.

....
[2]

[Total 6 marks]

Turn over ▶

10   The graph shows the volume of gas produced over time when lumps of zinc are reacted with dilute sulfuric acid.

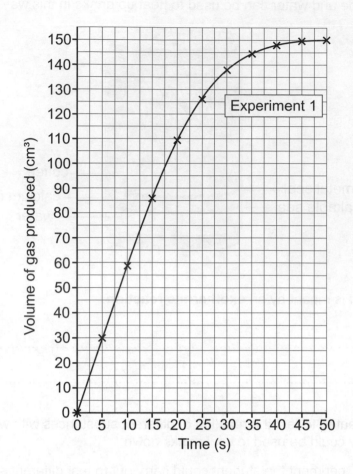

(a)   Use the graph to calculate the rate of reaction at 25 s.

rate of reaction = ... cm³/s

[3]

In a second experiment, some copper sulfate catalyst was added to the acid.
The same amount of zinc was used as before, and the lumps were of a similar size.
The same volume of dilute sulfuric acid was also used.

The results are shown in the table below.

Time (secs)	Volume of gas formed (cm³) Experiment 2
0	0
5	50
10	100
15	130
20	143
25	148
30	150
35	150
40	150
45	150
50	150

(b)   Plot the results of the second experiment on the graph on the previous page.
Draw a curve of best fit through the points. Label the line 'Experiment 2'.

[2]

(c)   How long does it take to form half of the total amount of gas collected
in the second experiment?

time taken = ... s

[1]

(d)   Describe what the curves show about how the rate of reaction changes as
the reaction proceeds.

....

[1]

(e)   State how the catalyst affects the reaction rate and explain how you can tell this from
the graph.

....

....

....

[1]

Turn over ▶

Practice Paper 1C

(f)   Explain, in terms of activation energy, how catalysts affect reaction rates.

....

....

....

[1]

[Total 9 marks]

11   Iron pipes need protection from rusting.

(a)   State the conditions that cause iron to rust.

....

....

[2]

(b)   Rusting is a type of corrosion. What causes corrosion?

☐ **A**   distillation

☐ **B**   electrolysis

☐ **C**   oxidation

☐ **D**   reduction

[1]

(c)   Paint can be used to stop underground iron pipes rusting, but they will eventually need repainting or replacing. An alternative to this is to connect a large piece of magnesium to the pipe, as shown in the diagram below.

Magnesium block

Insulated copper wire

Iron pipe

(i)   State the name given to this kind of corrosion protection.

....

[1]

(ii)   Explain why the magnesium protects the iron from rusting, and how this happens.

....

....

....

[2]

(d)   A coat of zinc could be applied to the iron pipes to prevent them rusting.
State the name given to this method of corrosion protection.

....

[1]

[Total 7 marks]

Turn over ▶

110

12 The balanced equation below shows what happens when a strip of magnesium metal is dissolved in a solution of hydrochloric acid.

$$Mg_{(s)} + 2HCl_{(aq)} \rightarrow MgCl_{2(aq)} + H_{2(g)}$$

(a) A student dissolved a piece of magnesium in an excess of hydrochloric acid.
7.60 g of $MgCl_2$ was produced. What mass of magnesium did the student start with?

Mass of magnesium = ... g

[3]

(b) Describe how the student could test for the gas produced in this reaction, and state what he would observe.

Test ....

....

Observation ....

....

[2]

(c) The student repeated the reaction, but added a few drops of methyl orange indicator to the acid before adding a magnesium strip.
Suggest a reason why no colour change occurred during the course of the reaction.

....

[1]

[Total 6 marks]

13 A student burns a piece of copper in air.

(a) The copper reacts with oxygen in the air to form copper oxide.
Use the data in the table below to find the empirical formula of the copper oxide.

Mass of empty container	28.00 g
Mass of container + mass of copper oxide	34.36 g
Mass of container + copper	33.08 g

Empirical formula = ...

[5]

(b) In another experiment, the student burns 1.08 g of magnesium in air.
She expected to produce 1.80 g of magnesium oxide.
The actual mass of magnesium oxide produced was 1.20 g.

(i) Calculate the percentage yield of magnesium oxide.

Percentage yield = ... %

[2]

(ii) Suggest a reason why the mass of magnesium oxide produced was less than expected.

....

....

[1]

[Total 8 marks]

[Total for paper 110 marks]

Candidate Surname		Candidate Forename(s)	

Centre Number	Candidate Number

Edexcel
International GCSE

Chemistry
Paper 2C

Practice Paper
Time allowed: 1 hour 15 minutes

You must have:
- A ruler.
- A calculator.

Total marks:

Instructions to candidates
- Use **black** ink to write your answers.
- Write your name and other details in the spaces provided above.
- Answer **all** questions in the spaces provided.
- In calculations, show clearly how you worked out your answers.
- You will need to answer some questions by placing a cross in a box, like this: ☒
  To change your answer, draw a line through the box like this: ☒
  Then mark your new answer as normal.

Information for candidates
- The marks available are given in brackets at the end of each question.
- There are 70 marks available for this paper.

Advice for candidates
- Read all the questions carefully.
- Write your answers as clearly and neatly as possible.
- Keep in mind how much time you have left.

Answer **all** questions

1   The diagram shows the electronic structures of a sodium atom and a chlorine atom.

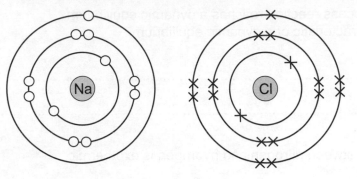

(a)   Chlorine has two major isotopes, ^{35}Cl and ^{37}Cl.
These isotopes are used to calculate the relative atomic mass of chlorine.

(i)   State what is meant by the term **isotope**.

....

....
[1]

(ii) ^{35}Cl has a relative abundance of 75%.

The relative atomic mass of chlorine is 35.5. Show how this value is calculated.

....

....
[2]

(b)   Sodium and chlorine react to form the ionic compound sodium chloride.

Draw a dot and cross diagram of sodium chloride. Show only the outer electrons.

[3]

[Total 6 marks]

Turn over ▶

2   The Haber process is used to make ammonia from nitrogen and hydrogen.
     The chemical equation for the reaction is:

$$N_{2(g)} + 3H_{2(g)} \rightleftharpoons 2NH_{3(g)}$$

(a)   The Haber process reaction reaches a dynamic equilibrium.
      State **one** characteristic of a dynamic equilibrium.

      ....

      ....
                                                                                          [1]

(b)   The reaction between nitrogen and hydrogen is exothermic.

      Explain what will happen to the yield of ammonia if the temperature
      is increased at constant pressure.

      ....

      ....

      ....
                                                                                          [2]

(c)   Explain what will happen to the yield of ammonia if the pressure is
      decreased at constant temperature.

      ....

      ....

      ....
                                                                                          [2]

(d)   At a particular pressure and temperature, the Haber process
      was used to produce 85 g of ammonia.

   (i)   Calculate the number of moles of ammonia produced.

                                                          Number of moles = ...
                                                                                          [2]

   (ii) Calculate the volume of this amount of ammonia at room temperature and pressure.

                                                          Volume = ... dm³
                                                                                          [1]
                                                                              [Total 8 marks]

3 The structural formula of an alcohol is shown below.

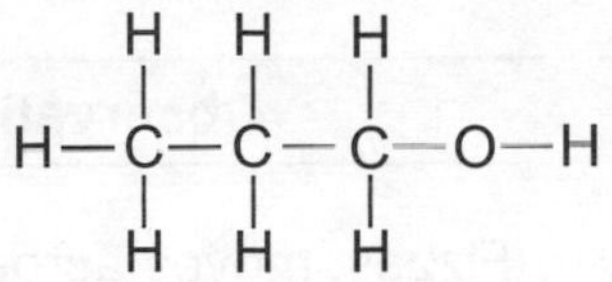

$$H-\underset{\underset{H}{|}}{\overset{\overset{H}{|}}{C}}-\underset{\underset{H}{|}}{\overset{\overset{H}{|}}{C}}-\underset{\underset{H}{|}}{\overset{\overset{H}{|}}{C}}-O-H$$

(a) Name the alcohol shown above.

....

[1]

(b) This alcohol can be used to make propyl propanoate.
The symbol equation for the formation of propyl propanoate is shown below.

$$C_3H_7OH + C_2H_5COOH \rightarrow C_2H_5COOC_3H_7 + H_2O$$

(i) Name the compound C_2H_5COOH.

....

[1]

(ii) State the homologous series of propyl propanoate.

....

[1]

(iii) Propyl propanoate has a strong, fruity smell.
Suggest **one** other property of propyl propanoate.

....

[1]

(c) Ethanol is another alcohol. Ethanol can be oxidised by burning in air.

(i) Write down a balanced symbol equation for the complete combustion of ethanol.

....

[2]

(ii) Suggest another method that can be used to oxidise ethanol.

....

....

[1]

[Total 7 marks]

Turn over ▶

Practice Paper 2C

4 A student investigates the reactions of the Group 1 elements lithium, sodium and potassium, with water. The student's observations are recorded in the table below.

Metal	Observations
lithium	Fizzes, moves across the surface
sodium	Fizzes strongly, melts into a round ball, moves across the surface
potassium	Fizzes violently, melts into a round ball, moves across the surface, a flame is seen

The student decides that the order of reactivity of the three elements is:

- potassium (most reactive)

- sodium

- lithium (least reactive)

(a) Give **two** pieces of evidence from the table that support the student's conclusion.

1 ....

....

2 ....

....

[2]

(b) Explain the pattern of reactivity that the student has noticed.

....

....

....

....

[2]

(c) Write a balanced chemical equation for the reaction between lithium and water.

....

[2]

(d)   The student accidentally mixes up some unlabelled samples of lithium chloride and potassium chloride. The student decides to do a test to find out which is which, using a moistened wire loop. Briefly describe the test that the student could carry out, and what the results would be.

....

....

....

[2]

[Total 8 marks]

Turn over ▶

5   Hydrogen can be burned in oxygen and used as a fuel.

$$2H_2 + O_2 \rightarrow 2H_2O$$

(a)   Calculate the enthalpy change for the reaction. The bond energy values are given below.

Bond energy values (kJ/mol):

O=O   +498

H–H   +436

O–H   +464

Enthalpy change = ... kJ/mol

[4]

(b)   Is bond breaking an exothermic or endothermic process?

....

[1]

(c)   In another reaction, the energy change is exothermic.
Which of the following energy profiles show the enthalpy change of the reaction?

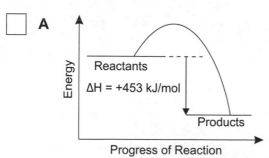

A

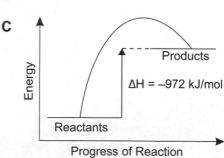

C

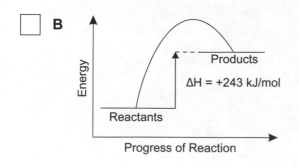

B

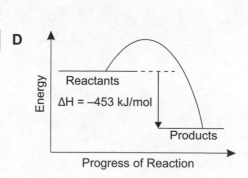

D

[1]

[Total 6 marks]

6   A student is investigating how the rate of the reaction between magnesium
     strips and hydrochloric acid is affected by the concentration of the acid.
     The student compares different concentrations of acid by measuring how
     long it takes for the reaction to produce 20 cm³ of hydrogen gas.

     The results of the experiment are shown below.

Concentration of acid (mol/dm³)	Time (s)
0.2	58
0.4	29
0.6	18
0.8	15
1.0	12

(a)   Plot the results on the axes below and draw a curve of best fit.

[2]

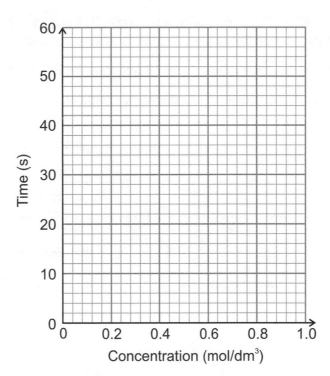

(b)   Use your graph to predict the time that it would take for 20 cm³ of hydrogen gas to form with
       0.5 mol/dm³ hydrochloric acid.

       .... s

       [1]

Turn over ▶

Practice Paper 2C

(c)   How could the student make his results more reliable?

....

[1]

(d)   Describe what the graph shows about the effect of concentration on the rate of reaction.

....

....

[1]

(e)   Explain, in terms of collision theory, why concentration affects the rate of a reaction.

....

....

....

....

[2]

(f)   The student carries out the experiment again using 0.6 mol/dm^3 hydrochloric acid.
This time, magnesium powder is used rather than strips of metal.

The student says "it will take longer than 18 seconds for 20 cm^3 of hydrogen gas to form".

Is the student's prediction correct? Explain your answer.

....

....

....

....

....

[3]

[Total 10 marks]

7   Titration with 0.050 mol/dm³ sulfuric acid was used to determine the concentration of calcium hydroxide solution. In the titration, 8.80 cm³ of sulfuric acid were needed to neutralise 10.0 cm³ of the calcium hydroxide solution.

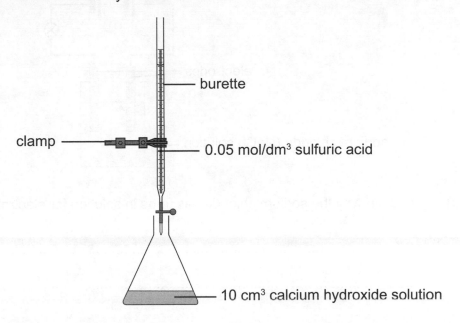

(a)   Name a suitable indicator for the titration.

....
                                                                                                                                        [1]

(b)   Complete and balance the equation for this reaction below.

$$H_2SO_{4(aq)} + Ca(OH)_{2(aq)} \rightarrow \text{...............}_{(aq)} + \text{...............}H_2O_{(l)}$$
                                                                                                                                        [2]

(c) (i)   How many moles of sulfuric acid reacted with the calcium hydroxide in the titration?

                                                                Number of moles = ...
                                                                                                                                        [1]

    (ii)   How many moles of calcium hydroxide reacted with the acid?

    ....
                                                                                                                                        [1]

    (iii)   Calculate the concentration of the calcium hydroxide solution in mol/dm³.
            Show clearly how you work out your answer.

                                                                Concentration = ... mol/dm³
                                                                                                                                        [1]
                                                                                                                            [Total 6 marks]

Turn over ▶

Practice Paper 2C

8   A student is doing an experiment to investigate the electrolysis of sodium chloride solution.

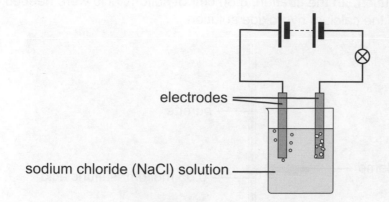

electrodes

sodium chloride (NaCl) solution

(a)   Explain why the sodium chloride has to be in solution for electrolysis to occur.

....

....

[2]

(b)   Write the half-equation for the reaction occurring at the positive electrode.

....

[1]

(c)   Why is sodium not formed at the negative electrode?

....

....

[1]

(d)   State the product that remains in solution.

....

[1]

Electrolysis can be used to extract aluminium from aluminium oxide.

(e)   Some metals can also be extracted from their oxides in a reduction reaction with carbon. Give a reason why aluminium cannot be extracted using this method.

....

....

[1]

f)   Aluminium is used as a material in the bodies of aircraft.
     Give **one** property of aluminium which would make it suitable for this application.

     ....

     ....
                                                                                                                    [1]

g)   The equation for the electrolysis of aluminium oxide is shown below:

$$2Al_2O_3 \rightarrow 4Al + 3O_2$$

     A scientist carries out an experiment where aluminium oxide is electrolysed.
     The scientist starts off with 40.8 g of pure aluminium oxide.
     Predict the mass of aluminium she can extract from this mass of electrolyte.

                                                              mass = ... g
                                                                                                                    [4]
                                                                                                [Total 11 marks]

Turn over ▶

Practice Paper 2C

9   Soluble salts can be made by reacting an acid with an insoluble base or an alkali.

(a)   An excess of zinc oxide is added to a beaker of dilute hydrochloric acid.
The mixture is stirred and the acid is neutralised.

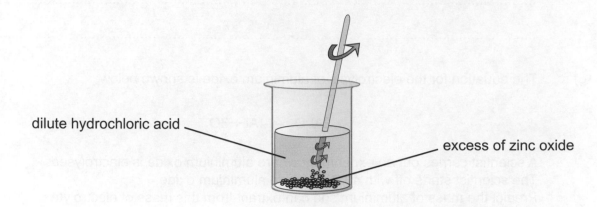

dilute hydrochloric acid

excess of zinc oxide

(i)   How could you tell when all the acid has been neutralised?

....

    [1]

(ii)   Give the products of this reaction.

....

    [2]

(b)   Describe how you could obtain a pure, dry sample of calcium chloride
from the alkali calcium hydroxide and dilute hydrochloric acid.

....

....

....

....

....

....

    [3]

(c)   Which **two** substances from the list below could be mixed to obtain barium sulfate by precipitation? Write the letters of the substances.

   A $CaSO_4$

   B $BaCl_2$

   C $BaCO_3$

   D $PbSO_4$

   E Na_2SO_4

   F $Ba(OH)_2$

   Substances .... and ....

[2]

[Total 8 marks]

[Total for paper 70 marks]

Answers

Section 1 — Particles and Mixtures

Page 4 — States of Matter

1 a)   solid *[1 mark]*
  b)   liquid *[1 mark]*
  c)   The particles in a gas move constantly with random motion in straight lines *[1 mark]*.
2 a)   D *[1 mark]*
  b)   evaporation *[1 mark]*
  c)   The particles gain energy *[1 mark]* and vibrate more *[1 mark]*. This weakens the forces that hold the solid together and makes the solid expand *[1 mark]*. At the point of melting, many of the particles have enough energy to break free from their positions *[1 mark]*.

Page 5 — Movement of Particles

1 a)   diffusion *[1 mark]*
  b)   D *[1 mark]*
  c)   B *[1 mark]*
2   Both jars will be the same paler brown colour *[1 mark]* because the random motion of the bromine and air particles means that they will eventually be equally mixed throughout both jars *[1 mark]*.

Page 6 — Solubility

1 a)   A mixture of a solute and a solvent *[1 mark]* that does not separate out *[1 mark]*.
  b)   The solution had become saturated, so no more sodium chloride can dissolve *[1 mark]*.
2 a)

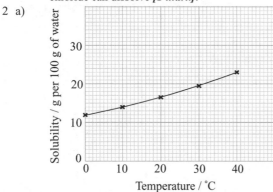

[1 mark for each correct labelled axis, 1 mark for all points correctly plotted, 1 mark for an appropriate line of best fit.]
  b)   18 g per 100 g of water *[1 mark. Accept answers between 17.5 and 18.5 g per 100 g of water.]*

Page 7 — Investigating Solubility

1 a)   B *[1 mark]*
  b)   E.g. if the solution was heated using a Bunsen burner, this could cause a fire hazard *[1 mark]*. The risk could be reduced by standing the Bunsen burner on a heat proof mat *[1 mark]*.
  c)   solubility (g per 100 g of solvent) = mass of solid (g) ÷ mass of water removed (g) × 100 = (12.2 g ÷ 32.8 g) × 100 = 37.1951... = **37.2 g per 100 g of solvent**
[2 marks for correct answer, otherwise 1 mark for correct working.]
  d)   E.g. repeating the experiment would improve the reliability *[1 mark]*.
  e)   The solubility of the substance *[1 mark]*.

Page 8 — Atoms

1 a)

Particle	Relative mass	Charge
Proton	**1**	+1
Neutron	1	**0**
Electron	**0.0005**	−1

[1 mark for each correct answer]
An electron's mass is tiny — you'd also get a mark for saying 'negligible'.
  b)   a molecule *[1 mark]*
2 a)   mass number = 55 *[1 mark]*
      atomic number = 25 *[1 mark]*
  b)   protons = 25 *[1 mark]*
      neutrons = mass number − atomic number
             = 55 − 25 = **30** *[1 mark]*
      electrons = 25 *[1 mark]*
3 a)   the nucleus *[1 mark]*
  b)   E.g.

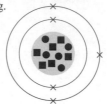

[1 mark for the protons, 1 mark for the neutrons.]

Page 9 — Isotopes and Relative Atomic Mass

1 a)   Isotopes are different atomic forms of the same element, which have the same number of protons *[1 mark]* but a different number of neutrons *[1 mark]*.
  b)

Isotope	Mass number	Number of protons	Number of neutrons
^{35}Cl	35	17	**18**
^{37}Cl	**37**	**17**	20

[1 mark for correctly stating the mass number and number of protons in ^{37}Cl, 1 mark for correctly finding the number of neutrons in both ^{35}Cl and ^{37}Cl.]
As ^{35}Cl and ^{37}Cl are isotopes of the same element, they must have the same number of protons.
2 a)   The relative atomic mass of an element is the average mass of all isotopes of the element *[1 mark]*, compared to the mass of one atom of carbon-12 *[1 mark]*.
  b)   E.g. relative atomic mass is an average value/result of a calculation *[1 mark]*.
3   % isotopic abundance of Ga-71 = 100 − 60.1 = 39.9
     relative atomic mass = (69 × 60.1) + (71 × 39.9) ÷ 100
     = (4146.9 + 2832.9) ÷ 100 = **69.8**
[3 marks for correct answer, otherwise 1 mark for working out % abundance of Ga-71, 1 mark for correctly substituting in values for abundances and atomic masses.]

Page 10 — Elements, Compounds and Mixtures

1   E.g. elements consist of one type of atom only *[1 mark]*, but compounds are made of two or more different elements which are chemically bonded together *[1 mark]*.

2   Sample A *[1 mark]*. The purer the substance, the smaller the range of the melting point / pure substances have sharp melting points, whereas impure substances melt over a range of temperatures *[1 mark]*.

3   Water vapour is a compound *[1 mark]*, because it is made up of two different elements which are chemically bonded together *[1 mark]*.
Liquid oxygen is an element *[1 mark]*, because it consists of one type of atom only *[1 mark]*.

Pages 11-13 — Separating Mixtures

1   brown seaweed *[1 mark]*

2 a)   A: fractionating column *[1 mark]*
    B: condenser *[1 mark]*

b)   The different liquids in the mixture will all have different boiling points *[1 mark]*. When the mixture is heated, the liquid with the lowest boiling point will evaporate first and it will reach the top of the fractionating column when the temperature there matches its boiling point *[1 mark]*. It can then be condensed and collected *[1 mark]*. When the first liquid has been collected, the temperature can be raised until the next liquid evaporates and reaches the top of the column, and so on *[1 mark]*.

3 a)   Distance from baseline to spot B = 2.4 cm / 24 mm *[1 mark]*
Distance from baseline to furthest point of solvent = 4.0 cm / 40 mm *[1 mark]*
R_f = distance travelled by solute ÷ distance travelled by solvent
= 2.4 ÷ 4.0 = **0.6**
[1 mark for correctly dividing measured distance to spot B by measured distance to solvent front.]

b) i)   E.g. draw a pencil line near the bottom of a sheet of filter paper and add spots of the different inks, including the ink from the document, to the line at intervals *[1 mark]*.
Put the paper in a beaker of solvent, e.g. water *[1 mark]*, so that the pencil line and the spots of ink are above the solvent *[1 mark]*.

ii)   The ink from the printer that produced the document will have the same R_f values as the ink from the document *[1 mark]*.

4 a)   Filtration *[1 mark]* would separate sodium chloride and ethanol, as the liquid ethanol would flow through the filter paper, leaving behind the solid sodium chloride *[1 mark]*. However, a mixture of sodium chloride and water is a solution, so both the water and dissolved sodium chloride would pass through the filter paper *[1 mark]*.

b)   E.g. simple distillation *[1 mark]*. Water and ethanol would both evaporate off and leave behind the solid sodium chloride *[1 mark]*.

5   The difference in the boiling points of ethanol and cyclopentane is quite large, so you could separate them using simple distillation *[1 mark]*. But the boiling points of ethanol and ethyl ethanoate are similar, so you would need to use fractional distillation to separate them *[1 mark]*.

Section 2 — The Periodic Table and Bonding

Page 14 — The Periodic Table

1 a)   A *[1 mark]*
b)   periods *[1 mark]*

2 a) i)   F *[1 mark]*
ii)   Kr *[1 mark]*
iii)   K *[1 mark]*

b)   beryllium/calcium *[1 mark]*, because it has the same number of electrons in its outer shell as magnesium *[1 mark]*.

Page 15 — Electron Shells

1   C *[1 mark]*
The electronic structure of neon is 2.8, so has 8 electrons in its outer shell.

2 a)   2.8.6 *[1 mark]*
b)

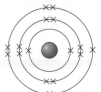

[1 mark]

3 a)   The group number tells you how many electrons are in the outer shell, so magnesium has 2 outer shell electrons *[1 mark]*. The period number tells you how many electron shells the atom has in total, so magnesium has three shells *[1 mark]*. All the shells apart from the outer shell will be filled (the first holds 2 electrons and the second holds 8) *[1 mark]*.

b)   2.8.2 *[1 mark]*

Page 16 — More on the Periodic Table

1 a)   B *[1 mark]*
b)   D *[1 mark]*
c)   To the right of the line *[1 mark]*. Since it does not conduct electricity, it must be a non-metal *[1 mark]*.

2   Argon won't easily give up or gain electrons, making it inert *[1 mark]*. This means that it won't react with the metal filament in the light bulb *[1 mark]*.

Page 17 — Ionic Bonding

1   A *[1 mark]*

2 a)   The oppositely charged ions are strongly attracted to each other *[1 mark]* by electrostatic attractions/forces *[1 mark]*.

b) i) K^+ *[1 mark]*
ii) Cl^- *[1 mark]*
Group 1 elements lose 1 electron to form positive ions. Group 7 elements gain 1 electron to form negative ions.

3 a)   The number of electrons gained is equal to 8 – the group number *[1 mark]*. Sulfur is in Group 6, so 8 – 6 = 2 electrons gained. Chlorine is in Group 7, so 8 – 7 = 1 electron gained *[1 mark]*.

b)   Both nitrate and bromide ions are negatively charged *[1 mark]*. Ionic compounds can only be formed between negative and positive ions *[1 mark]*.

Pages 18-19 — Ionic Compounds

1 a)

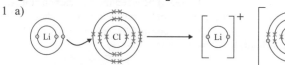

[1 mark for arrow showing electron transfer from Li to Cl, 1 mark for adding seven crosses and one dot to outer shell of the chloride ion, 1 mark for correct charges on both ions.]

b)   neutral/no overall charge *[1 mark]*

2 a)   D *[1 mark]*
  b)   giant ionic lattice *[1 mark]*
3   positive: Al³⁺ *[1 mark]*
      negative: F⁻ *[1 mark]*
4   magnesium hydroxide: Mg(OH)₂ *[1 mark]*
      potassium nitrate: KNO₃ *[1 mark]*
5

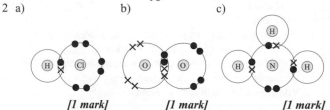

*[1 mark for correct electronic structure of sodium ions,
1 mark for correct electronic structure of oxygen ion,
1 mark for correct charge on oxygen ion, 1 mark for
correct charge on sodium ions.]*

*It's fine if you just drew the outer shell of electrons on the atoms —
you'd still get the marks in the exam.*

6 a)   Sodium chloride contains positive sodium ions (Na⁺)
      [1 mark] and negative chloride ions (Cl⁻) *[1 mark]* that are
      arranged in a giant ionic lattice *[1 mark]*. The oppositely
      charged ions are held together by a strong electrostatic
      attraction *[1 mark]*.
  b)   To melt sodium chloride, you have to overcome the very
      strong electrostatic forces/ionic bonds between the ions
      [1 mark], which requires lots of energy *[1 mark]*.

Pages 20-21 — Covalent Bonding

1 a)   8 *[1 mark]*
  b)   3 *[1 mark]*
  c)   0 *[1 mark]*

*All the bonds in the molecule are single covalent bonds — you get double
bonds in molecules like ethene, oxygen and carbon dioxide.*

2 a)   b)   c)

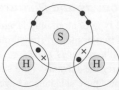

      [1 mark]   *[1 mark]*   *[1 mark]*

3   A silicon atom has four electrons in its outer shell *[1 mark]*.
      So a silicon atom can form four covalent bonds *[1 mark]*.

4 a)

*[1 mark for the C-C shared pair, 1 mark for all of the
H-C shared pairs correct.]*

  b)   There is a pair of shared electrons between each hydrogen
      atom and a carbon atom, and between the two carbon atoms
      [1 mark]. Strong electrostatic attractions between these
      (negatively charged) electrons and the (positive) nuclei of the
      atoms hold the atoms together *[1 mark]*.

5

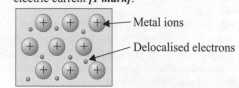

*[1 mark for both shared pairs, 1 mark for the non-bonding
electrons.]*

Page 22 — Covalent Substances

1   D *[1 mark]* — giant covalent substances have high melting
      points and don't normally conduct electricity, even when
      molten *[1 mark]*.
2   In a giant covalent structure, all of the atoms are bonded to
      each other with strong covalent bonds *[1 mark]*. It takes
      lots of energy to break the many bonds and melt the solid
      [1 mark].
3 a)   A — graphite *[1 mark]*
      B — C₆₀ fullerene *[1 mark]*
      C — diamond *[1 mark]*
  b)   Graphite/structure A can conduct electricity because
      it contains delocalised electrons that can move around
      [1 mark]. Diamond/structure C doesn't conduct electricity
      because it doesn't contain any charged particles that can
      move around *[1 mark]*. Diamond/structure C is hard because
      the strong covalent bonds hold the atoms in a rigid lattice
      structure *[1 mark]*. Graphite/structure A is soft, as the layers
      of graphite are held together by weak intermolecular forces
      [1 mark].
  c)   Structure B is a simple molecular substance *[1 mark]* so only
      weak intermolecular forces need to be broken to separate
      the molecules *[1 mark]*. In order for A to sublime, strong
      covalent bonds need to be broken, which would require more
      energy *[1 mark]*.

Page 23 — Electrical Conductivity and Metals

1 a)

State	Conducts electricity? (yes/no)
Solid	No *[1 mark]*
Dissolved in water	Yes *[1 mark]*
Molten	Yes *[1 mark]*

  b)   When it is molten or in solution it conducts electricity
      because the ions separate and are free to move about
      [1 mark], so they can carry electric current. When it is solid
      it doesn't conduct electricity because the ions are held rigidly
      and aren't free to move and carry electric current *[1 mark]*.
  c)   E.g. covalent compounds make bonds by sharing electrons so
      they don't contain ions *[1 mark]*. This means that they don't
      have any charge carriers that are free to move and carry an
      electric current *[1 mark]*.

2 a)

*[1 mark for regular arrangement of metal ions,
1 mark for delocalised electrons, 1 mark for labels]*

  b)   E.g. metals are good conductors of electricity because the
      delocalised electrons in the structure carry electrical current
      [1 mark]. Most metals are malleable because the layers of
      atoms in metals can slide over each other allowing them to be
      hammered or rolled into sheets *[1 mark]*.

Section 3 — Equations, Calculations and Electrolysis

Pages 24-25 — Balancing Equations

1   C *[1 mark]*

2 a)   methane + oxygen → carbon dioxide + water
    [1 mark]

  b) $CH_4 + 2O_2 \rightarrow CO_2 + 2H_2O$
    [1 mark for the correct reactants and products, 1 mark for correctly balancing the equation]

For any question that involves balancing an equation, you would also get the mark if you have matching multiples of the correct numbers.

3    $Cl_2 + 2KBr \rightarrow Br_2 + 2KCl$
    [1 mark for the correct reactants and products, 1 mark for correctly balancing the equation]

4 a) i) $2HCl + CuO \rightarrow CuCl_2 + H_2O$ *[1 mark]*
    ii) $2HNO_3 + MgO \rightarrow Mg(NO_3)_2 + H_2O$ *[1 mark]*

  b) $6HCl + 2Al \rightarrow 2AlCl_3 + 3H_2$
    [1 mark for the correct reactants and products, 1 mark for correctly balancing the equation]

5 a) $2CuO + C \rightarrow 2Cu + CO_2$ *[1 mark]*

  b) $3CO + Fe_2O_3 \rightarrow 3CO_2 + 2Fe$ *[1 mark]*

6 a) $2Na + Cl_2 \rightarrow 2NaCl$
    [1 mark for the correct reactants and products, 1 mark for correctly balancing the equation]

  b) $Ca(OH)_{2(aq)} + Na_2CO_{3(s)} \rightarrow 2NaOH_{(aq)} + CaCO_{3(s)}$
    [1 mark for all state symbols correct]

  c) $2Na_{(s)} + 2H_2O_{(l)} \rightarrow 2NaOH_{(aq)} + H_{2(g)}$
    [1 mark for correct reactants and products, 1 mark for correctly balancing the equation, 1 mark for all state symbols correct]

7    $S + 6HNO_3 \rightarrow H_2SO_4 + 6NO_2 + 2H_2O$ *[1 mark]*

Page 26 — Relative Formula Mass

1   C *[1 mark]*

2    $Ca(OH)_2 = 40 + ((16 + 1) \times 2) =$ **74** *[2 marks for correct answer, otherwise 1 mark for correct working.]*

3    $Zn(CN)_2 = 65 + ((12 + 14) \times 2) =$ **117** *[2 marks for correct answer, otherwise 1 mark for correct working.]*

4    $2AOH + H_2 = 114$
    $2A + ((16 + 1) \times 2) + (1 \times 2) = 114$
    $2A + 34 + 2 = 114$
    $2A + 36 = 114$
    $2A = 78$
    $A = 39$
    So element A = potassium
    [3 marks for correct answer, otherwise 1 mark for correct working, 1 mark for correct A_r.]

Pages 27-28 — Moles

1   A *[1 mark]*

2   moles = mass ÷ $M_r = 9.0 ÷ 12 =$ **0.75 moles** *[1 mark]*

3    $M_r(C_9H_8O_4) = (12 \times 9) + (1 \times 8) + (16 \times 4) = 180$
    mass = moles × $M_r = 12.4 \times 180 =$ **2232 g**
    [2 marks for the correct answer, otherwise 1 mark for calculating the M_r of $C_9H_8O_4$.]

4 a) M_r = mass ÷ moles = $3.0 ÷ 0.075 =$ **40** *[1 mark]*

  b)   B *[1 mark]*

5 a) $M_r(ZnCO_3) = 65 + 12 + (16 \times 3) = 125$
    moles = mass ÷ $M_r = 275 ÷ 125 =$ **2.2 moles**
    [2 marks for the correct answer, otherwise 1 mark for calculating the M_r of $ZnCO_3$.]

  b) $M_r(HCl) = 1 + 35.5 = 36.5$
    mass = moles × $M_r = 6 \times 36.5 =$ **219 g**
    [2 marks for the correct answer, otherwise 1 mark for calculating the M_r of HCl.]

6    $M_r(Fe_2O_3) = (56 \times 2) + (16 \times 3) = 160$
    3.52 kg = 3520 g
    moles = mass ÷ $M_r = 3520 ÷ 160 =$ **22 moles**
    [3 marks for the correct answer, otherwise 1 mark for calculating the M_r of Fe_2O_3, 1 mark for converting between kg and g.]

7    $M_r(KOH) = 39 + 16 + 1 = 56$
    Mass of 4 moles of KOH = $4 \times 56 = 224$ g
    Extra mass needed = $224 - 140 =$ **84 g** *[2 marks for correct answer, otherwise 1 mark for correct working.]*

Pages 29-30 — Calculating Masses in Reactions

1 a) $M_r(Mg) = 24$
    $M_r(MgO) = 24 + 16 = 40$
    moles of Mg = mass ÷ $M_r = 12 ÷ 24 = 0.5$
    There is a 1:1 ratio between the number of moles of Mg and MgO in the balanced equation, so 0.5 moles of Mg react to give 0.5 moles of MgO.
    mass of MgO = moles × $M_r = 0.5 \times 40 =$ **20 g**
    [3 marks for correct answer, otherwise 1 mark for correctly calculating both M_rs, 1 mark for calculating the moles of Mg and MgO.]

  b) $M_r(Na_2O) = (23 \times 2) + 16 = 62$
    $M_r(Na) = 23$
    moles of Na_2O = mass ÷ $M_r = 6.2 ÷ 62 = 0.1$
    There is a 1:2 ratio between the number of moles of Na_2O and Na in the balanced equation, so 0.1 moles of Na_2O will be formed from 0.2 moles of Na.
    mass of Na = moles × $M_r = 0.2 \times 23 =$ **4.6 g**
    [3 marks for correct answer, otherwise 1 mark for correctly calculating both M_rs, 1 mark for calculating the moles of Na_2O and Na.]

2 a) $M_r(Fe_2O_3) = (56 \times 2) + (16 \times 3) = 160$
    $M_r(Fe) = 56$
    moles of Fe_2O_3 = mass ÷ $M_r = 20 ÷ 160 = 0.125$
    There is a 1:2 ratio between the number of moles of Fe_2O_3 and Fe in the balanced equation, so 0.125 moles of Fe_2O_3 react to give 0.25 moles of Fe.
    mass of Fe = moles × $M_r = 0.25 \times 56 =$ **14 g**
    [3 marks for correct answer, otherwise 1 mark for correctly calculating both M_rs, 1 mark for calculating the moles of Fe_2O_3 and Fe.]

  b) $M_r(Fe_2O_3) = (56 \times 2) + (16 \times 3) = 160$
    $M_r(Al) = 27$
    moles of Fe_2O_3 = mass ÷ $M_r = (32 \times 1000) ÷ 160 = 200$
    There is a 1:2 ratio between the number of moles of Fe_2O_3 and Al in the balanced equation, so 200 moles of Fe_2O_3 react with 400 moles of Al.
    mass of Al = moles × $M_r = 400 \times 27 = 10800$ g = **10.8 kg**
    [3 marks for correct answer, otherwise 1 mark for correctly calculating both M_rs, 1 mark for calculating the moles of Fe_2O_3 and Al.]

3 a) $M_r(Na_2SO_4) = (23 \times 2) + 32 + (16 \times 4) = 142$
    $M_r(NaOH) = 23 + 16 + 1 = 40$
    moles of Na_2SO_4 = mass ÷ $M_r = 71 ÷ 142 = 0.5$
    There is a 1:2 ratio between the number of moles of Na_2SO_4 and NaOH in the balanced equation, so 0.5 moles of Na_2SO_4 will be formed from 1 mole of NaOH.
    mass of NaOH = moles × $M_r = 1 \times 40 =$ **40 g**
    [3 marks for correct answer, otherwise 1 mark for correctly calculating both M_rs, 1 mark for calculating the moles of Na_2SO_4 and NaOH.]

b) $M_r(H_2SO_4) = (1 \times 2) + 32 + (16 \times 4) = 98$
$M_r(H_2O) = (1 \times 2) + 16 = 18$
moles of H_2SO_4 = mass ÷ M_r = 24.5 ÷ 98 = 0.25
There is a 1:2 ratio between the number of moles of H_2SO_4
and H_2O in the balanced equation, so 0.25 moles of H_2SO_4
react to give 0.5 moles of H_2O.
mass of H_2O = moles × M_r = 0.5 × 18 = **9 g**
*[3 marks for correct answer, otherwise 1 mark for correctly
calculating both M_rs, 1 mark for calculating the moles of
H_2SO_4 and H_2O.]*

4   Moles of CO produced from 10.2 g of C at stage 2:
$M_r(C) = 12$
moles of C = mass ÷ M_r = 10.2 ÷ 12 = 0.85
There is a 1:2 ratio between the number of moles of C and
CO in the balanced equation, so 0.85 moles of C will react to
produce 1.7 moles of CO.
Mass of CO_2 produced at stage 3:
There is a 1:1 ratio between the number of moles of CO and
CO_2 in the balanced equation, so 1.7 moles of CO will react
to produce 1.7 moles of CO_2.
$M_r(CO_2) = 12 + (16 \times 2) = 44$
mass of CO_2 = moles × M_r = 1.7 × 44 = **74.8 g**
*[5 marks for correct answer, otherwise 1 mark for
calculating the M_r of C and CO_2, 1 mark for correct moles
of C, 1 mark for correct moles of CO, 1 mark for correct
moles of CO_2.]*

Page 31 — Calculating Percentage Yield

1 a)   The yield of a reaction is the mass of product it produces
[1 mark].
  b)   percentage yield = (1.2 ÷ 1.6) × 100 = **75%** *[1 mark]*
2   percentage yield = (6 ÷ 15) × 100 = **40%** *[1 mark]*
3    $M_r(CaCO_3) = 40 + 12 + (16 \times 3) = 100$
$M_r(CaO) = 40 + 16 = 56$
Mass of $CaCO_3$ in g = 68.00 × 1000 = 68 000 g
Moles = mass ÷ M_r
Moles ($CaCO_3$) = 68 000 ÷ 100 = 680
1 mole of $CaCO_3$ produces 1 mole of CaO.
So 680 moles of $CaCO_3$ should produce 680 moles of CaO.
Theoretical yield = 680 × 56 = 38 080 g = 38.08 kg
Percentage yield = (28.56 ÷ 38.08) × 100 = **75%**
*[5 marks for correct answer, otherwise 1 mark for correctly
calculating M_rs, 1 mark for correct moles of $CaCO_3$ and
CaO, 1 mark for finding the theoretical yield of CaO,
1 mark for dividing actual yield by theoretical yield and
multiplying by 100.]*

*If you didn't convert the mass of $CaCO_3$ from kg to g you should still
have got the correct answer as long as you kept all the masses as kg
throughout your working. If your answer is wrong, you should still get
marks for your working.*

Page 32 — Empirical and Molecular Formulae

1   Number of moles: N = 30.4 ÷ 14 = 2.17
                         O = 69.6 ÷ 16 = 4.35
Simplest whole number ratio:
(2.17 ÷ 2.17) : (4.35 ÷ 2.17) = 1 : 2
Empirical formula: NO_2
*[3 marks for correct answer, otherwise 1 mark for correct
number of moles of each element, 1 mark for finding the
simplest whole number ratio.]*
2   Division by A_r: Al = 10.1 ÷ 27 = 0.37
                        Br = 89.9 ÷ 80 = 1.12
Simplest whole number ratio:
(0.37 ÷ 0.37) : (1.12 ÷ 0.37) = 1 : 3
Empirical formula: $AlBr_3$
*[3 marks for correct answer, otherwise 1 mark for dividing
the percentage of each element by the A_r, 1 mark for finding
the simplest whole number ratio.]*

3   Work out the mass of H: 1.48 − (0.8 + 0.64) = 0.04
Number of moles: Ca = 0.8 ÷ 40 = 0.02
                    O = 0.64 ÷ 16 = 0.04
                    H = 0.04 ÷ 1 = 0.04
Simplest whole number ratio:
(0.02 ÷ 0.02) : (0.04 ÷ 0.02) : (0.04 ÷ 0.02) = 1 : 2 : 2
Empirical formula: $Ca(OH)_2$ / CaO_2H_2
*[4 marks for correct answer, otherwise 1 mark for
calculating the mass of H, 1 mark for correct number of
moles of each element, 1 mark for finding the simplest
whole number ratio.]*
4   Calculate the mass of the empirical formula:
$(12 \times 3) + (1 \times 7) + 16 = 59$ *[1 mark]*
Divide the relative molecular mass by this mass:
118 ÷ 59 = 2 *[1 mark]*
Work out the molecular formula:
empirical formula × 2 = $C_6H_{14}O_2$ *[1 mark]*

Page 33 — Finding Formulae Using Experiments

1 a)   C *[1 mark]*
  b) i) mass of manganese = (mass of test tube and bung +
manganese) − (mass of test tube and bung)
= 84.88 − 36.48 = **48.40** *[1 mark]*
    ii) Number of moles: Mn = 48.40 ÷ 55 = 0.88
                          O = 14.08 ÷ 16 = 0.88 *[1 mark]*
Simplest whole number ratio:
(0.88 ÷ 0.88) : (0.88 ÷ 0.88) = 1 : 1 *[1 mark]*
Empirical formula: MnO *[1 mark]*
2 a)   E.g. a crucible *[1 mark]*.
  b)   mass of O = 5.440 − 3.808 = 1.632 g *[1 mark]*
Number of moles: Fe = 3.808 ÷ 56 = 0.068
                   O = 1.632 ÷ 16 = 0.102 *[1 mark]*
Simplest whole number ratio:
(0.068 ÷ 0.068) : (0.102 ÷ 0.068) = 1 : 1.5 = 2 : 3 *[1 mark]*
Empirical formula: Fe_2O_3 *[1 mark]*

Page 34 — Water of Crystallisation

1 a)   E.g. to remove all of the water from the salt *[1 mark]*.
  b) i) 61.224 − 53.500 = **7.724 g** *[1 mark]*
    ii) 56.364 − 53.500 = **2.864 g** *[1 mark]*
  c) M_r of Na_2CO_3 = (23 × 2) + 12 + (16 × 3) = 106 *[1 mark]*
Moles of water lost:
Mass of water lost = 7.724 − 2.864 = 4.86 g
Moles of water lost = 4.86 ÷ 18 = 0.27 *[1 mark]*
Moles of anhydrous salt produced:
Moles of Na_2CO_3 = 2.864 ÷ 106 = 0.027 *[1 mark]*
Ratio of salt to water:
0.027 moles of salt (Na_2CO_3) : 0.27 moles of water
1 mole of Na_2CO_3 : (0.27 ÷ 0.027) = 10 moles of water
x = **10** *[1 mark]*

Page 35 — Moles and Concentration

1 a)   Mean volume of HCl = (12.50 + 12.55 + 12.45) ÷ 3
= **12.50 cm³**
*[2 marks for correct answer, otherwise 1 mark for correct
equation to calculate the mean.]*
  b)   12.50 cm³ = 0.0125 dm³ *[1 mark]*
Moles = concentration × volume of solution
= 1.00 × 0.0125 = 0.0125 moles *[1 mark]*
2 a)   120 cm³ = 0.12 dm³
2.5 × 0.12 = **0.3 moles** *[1 mark]*
  b)   750 cm³ = 0.75 dm³
3 ÷ 0.75 = **4 mol/dm³** *[1 mark]*
  c) M_r of Na_2SO_4 = (23 × 2) + 32 + (16 × 4) = 142 *[1 mark]*
Mass = 4 × 142 = 568 g
Concentration in g/dm³ = **568 g/dm³** *[1 mark]*

Page 36 — Calculating Volume

1 a) 24 dm^3 / 24 000 cm^3 *[1 mark]*
  b) 1.5 × 24 = 36 dm^3 *[1 mark]*
2 2.25 ÷ 24 = 0.094 moles OR 2250 ÷ 24 000 = 0.094 moles
   [1 mark]
3 a) 2NO + O$_2$ → 2NO$_2$
   M_r(NO) = 14 + 16 = 30
   moles of NO = mass ÷ M_r = 7.8 ÷ 30 = 0.26
   There is a 1:1 ratio between the number of moles of NO and
   NO$_2$ in the balanced equation, so 0.26 moles of NO react to
   give 0.26 moles of NO$_2$.
   volume of NO$_2$ = moles × 24 = 0.26 × 24 = **6.24 dm^3**
   *[3 marks for correct answer, otherwise 1 mark for correct
   moles of NO, 1 mark for correct moles of NO$_2$.]*
  b) There is a 2:1 ratio between the number of moles of NO and
   O$_2$ in the balanced equation, so 0.26 moles of NO react with
   0.13 moles of O$_2$.
   volume of O$_2$ = moles × 24 = 0.13 × 24 = **3.12 dm^3**
   *[2 marks for correct answer, otherwise 1 mark for correct
   moles of O$_2$.]*

Page 37 — Electrolysis

1 a) D *[1 mark]*
  b) B *[1 mark]*
  c) C *[1 mark]*
  d) A *[1 mark]*
2 Negative electrode: Pb^{2+} + 2e$^-$ → Pb
   [1 mark for correct equation, 1 mark for correct balancing]
   Positive electrode: 2Br$^-$ → Br$_2$ + 2e$^-$
   [1 mark for correct equation, 1 mark for correct balancing]
3 a) Negative electrode: potassium *[1 mark]*
   Positive electrode: iodine *[1 mark]*
  b) It is oxidation, as the iodide ions lose electrons *[1 mark]*.

Pages 38-39 — Electrolysis of Aqueous Solutions

1 a) 2H$^+$ + 2e$^-$ → H$_2$ *[1 mark]*
   2Cl$^-$ → Cl$_2$ + 2e$^-$ *[1 mark]*
  b) 4OH$^-$ → O$_2$ + 2H$_2$O + 4e$^-$ *[1 mark]*
  c) cathode *[1 mark]*
2 a) B *[1 mark]*
  b) e.g. platinum/graphite *[1 mark]*
  c) i) Bubbles of chlorine gas would form *[1 mark]*.
   ii) Copper metal would coat the electrode *[1 mark]*.
3 a) E.g.

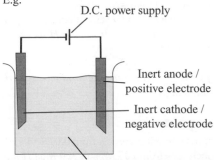

D.C. power supply

Inert anode /
positive electrode

Inert cathode /
negative electrode

Aqueous solution / electrolyte

   *[1 mark for power supply, 1 mark for electrodes in solution,
   1 mark for labels]*
  b) i) Cu^{2+} *[1 mark]*, SO$_4$$^{2-}$ *[1 mark]*, H$^+$ *[1 mark]*, OH$^-$ *[1 mark]*
   ii) Cu^{2+} + 2e$^-$ → Cu *[1 mark for correct reactants and
   products, 1 mark for correct balancing.]*
  c) Potassium is more reactive than hydrogen *[1 mark]* so
   hydrogen is produced *[1 mark]*. There are no halide ions
   [1 mark] so oxygen and water are produced *[1 mark]*.

Section 4 — Inorganic Chemistry

Page 40 — Group 1 — The Alkali Metals

1 a) Metal B is the most reactive *[1 mark]* because it takes
   the least time to react completely with the water *[1 mark]*.
  b) **A** = sodium, **B** = potassium and **C** = lithium.
   *[2 marks for all three answers correct, otherwise 1 mark for
   any one answer correct.]*
  c) sodium hydroxide *[1 mark]*, hydrogen *[1 mark]*
  d) Rubidium is further down the group than potassium/metal B
   [1 mark], so it is more reactive/will take less time to react
   [1 mark].
2 As you go down Group 1, the outer electron is further
   from the nucleus *[1 mark]*, which means it is less strongly
   attracted to the nucleus *[1 mark]*. So as you go down
   Group 1 the outer electron is more easily lost *[1 mark]*.

Page 41 — Group 7 — The Halogens

1 a) Chlorine — green *[1 mark]*
   Iodine — solid *[1 mark]*
  b) i) Fluorine is more reactive than chlorine *[1 mark]*.
   ii) gas *[1 mark]*
2 a) The halogens have seven electrons in their outer shell
   [1 mark]. As you go further down the group additional shells
   are added / the outer electrons are further away from the
   nucleus *[1 mark]*.
  b) Both astatine and fluorine have 7 outer shell electrons so
   should react in a similar way *[1 mark]*. So astatine should
   react with sodium to form sodium astatide *[1 mark]*.
   But astatine would react more slowly than fluorine, as it
   would be less reactive *[1 mark]*. This is because it would be
   more difficult for astatine to attract extra electrons/form ions,
   as the extra electron would be added to a shell further away
   from the nucleus *[1 mark]*.

Page 42 — Displacement Reactions

1 a) A displacement reaction is where a more reactive element
   displaces a less reactive element from a compound *[1 mark]*.
  b) i) A reaction where reduction and oxidation happen at the
   same time, and so one substance loses electrons and another
   substance gains electrons *[1 mark]*.
   ii) iodide/I$^-$ *[1 mark]*
   iii) bromine/Br *[1 mark]*
2 a) Before — colourless *[1 mark]*
   After — brown *[1 mark]*
  b) Yes *[1 mark]*, as chlorine is more reactive than astatine
   [1 mark].

Page 43 — Gases in the Atmosphere

1 a) i) argon *[1 mark]*
   ii) oxygen *[1 mark]*
   iii) nitrogen *[1 mark]*
  b) i) 78% (accept 77-79%) *[1 mark]*
   ii) 0.04% (accept 0.035-0.045%) *[1 mark]*
2 a) 28.0 − 21.7 = 6.3
   (6.3 ÷ 28.0) × 100 = **22.5%**
   *[2 marks for correct answer, otherwise 1 mark for correct
   working.]*
  b) E.g. use a measuring cylinder instead of a test tube *[1 mark]*
   as this will give a more accurate measurement for the volume
   of air (as the volume of air can be read directly from the
   scale) *[1 mark]*.

Page 44 — Gases in Reactions

1 a) i) $CuCO_{3(s)} \rightarrow CuO_{(s)} + CO_{2(g)}$ *[1 mark]*
   ii) E.g. using a delivery tube and test tube. / Using a gas syringe. *[1 mark]*
   b) thermal decomposition *[1 mark]*
2 a) i) pale blue *[1 mark]*
   ii) acidic *[1 mark]*
   b) A bright white flame *[1 mark]* and the formation of white powder *[1 mark]*.
   c) $2H_2 + O_2 \rightarrow 2H_2O$
   [1 mark for the correct reactants and products, 1 mark for correct balancing.]

Page 45 — Carbon Dioxide

1 a) Heat detector B *[1 mark]*, e.g. because the nitrogen will absorb less heat than the carbon dioxide/the carbon dioxide will absorb more heat than the nitrogen *[1 mark]*.
   b) Carbon dioxide absorbs heat that would otherwise be radiated out into space *[1 mark]* and re-radiates some of it back towards the Earth *[1 mark]*.
2 a) There was an increase in CO_2 in the atmosphere between 1850 and 2000 *[1 mark]*. This is probably largely due to human activity (e.g. burning fossil fuels/deforestation) *[1 mark]*. The increase in CO_2 correlates with an increase in temperature over the same time period *[1 mark]*. The temperature increase is likely due to the increase in CO_2 as CO_2 is a greenhouse gas / insulates the Earth *[1 mark]*.
   b) E.g. climate change / changing rainfall patterns / sea level rise / flooding *[1 mark]*
Be careful — you can't say 'global warming' here because that's just an alternative name for the temperature change, not an effect of it.

Pages 46-47 — Reactions of Metals

1 a) Most reactive: magnesium
                     zinc
                     iron
Least reactive: copper
   [1 mark for putting magnesium at the top and copper at the bottom. 1 mark for putting zinc above iron in the middle.]
   b) i) zinc oxide *[1 mark]*
   ii) Metal X was sodium, because it reacted vigorously with cold water *[1 mark]*.
2 a) $Mg + H_2SO_4 \rightarrow MgSO_4 + H_2$
   [1 mark for correct reactants, 1 mark for correct products.]
   b) A very vigorous fizzing/more vigorous than lithium *[1 mark]*, sodium disappears *[1 mark]*.
   c) lithium, calcium, copper *[1 mark]*
   d) It is not possible to tell the difference between magnesium and zinc from these results since both have the same reaction with dilute acid *[1 mark]*. E.g. to find which is more reactive, you could find the effect of adding zinc to water *[1 mark]*.

Pages 48-49 — The Reactivity Series

1 a) B *[1 mark]*
   b) D *[1 mark]*
2 a) e.g. iron *[1 mark]*
The unidentified metal must be more reactive than copper (as it displaces copper from copper sulfate), but less reactive than zinc (which it doesn't displace from zinc sulfate).
   b) The copper was displaced from its salt *[1 mark]*.
   c) Zinc is more reactive than copper *[1 mark]*.

3 a)

	aluminium oxide	copper oxide	iron oxide	magnesium oxide
aluminium	✗	✓	✓	✗
copper	✗	✗	✗	✗
iron	✗	✓	✗	✗
magnesium	✓	✓	✓	✗

[2 marks for all four answers correct, otherwise 1 mark for three correct.]
   b) none *[1 mark]*
   c) Magnesium *[1 mark]* as it is the most reactive metal in the table *[1 mark]*.
4 a) $Mg_{(s)} + FeCl_{2(aq)} \rightarrow MgCl_{2(aq)} + Fe_{(s)}$
   [1 mark for the correct reactants and products, 1 mark for all state symbols correct.]
   b) Magnesium is oxidised / loses electrons to form magnesium ions *[1 mark]* and simultaneously iron ions are reduced / gain electrons to form iron metal *[1 mark]*.
   c) The solution would turn from blue to colourless *[1 mark]*. A brown precipitate would form *[1 mark]*.

Page 50 — Iron

1 a) water *[1 mark]*, oxygen *[1 mark]*
Saying air instead of oxygen is unlikely to be specific enough to get the marks for a question like this — always be as precise as you can.
   b) tube B *[1 mark]*
   c) The painted nail would not rust *[1 mark]*, because the paint creates a barrier that keeps out water and oxygen *[1 mark]*.
2 a) Sacrificial protection involves attaching a metal that is more reactive than steel to the ship *[1 mark]*. The more reactive metal will lose electrons/be oxidised more easily than steel *[1 mark]*, so it will corrode instead of the steel *[1 mark]*.
   b) No, the zinc layer acts as sacrificial protection as well as a barrier / the zinc is more reactive than iron *[1 mark]* so it will lose electrons in preference to iron, even if it's scratched *[1 mark]*.

Page 51 — Metals and Redox

1 a) zinc oxide + carbon → zinc + carbon dioxide *[1 mark]*
   b) carbon *[1 mark]*
2 a) electrolysis *[1 mark]*
   b) If the metal is more reactive than carbon, it can't be extracted using carbon *[1 mark]*.
3 a) Many metals can react with other elements/oxygen to form compounds/oxides *[1 mark]*.
   b) Iron is lower in the reactivity series than carbon *[1 mark]*, so carbon can take oxygen away from iron *[1 mark]*.
   c) reduction *[1 mark]*
   d) $2Fe_2O_3 + 3C \rightarrow 4Fe + 3CO_2$
   [1 mark for correct reactants and products, 1 mark for correct balancing.]

Page 52 — Uses of Metals

1 a) As the carbon content increases from 0.07% to 1.6% the strength increases from 200 MPa to 350 Mpa *[1 mark]*.
   b) Atoms of different elements are different sizes *[1 mark]*. Adding atoms of a different size to a pure metal in alloys distorts the layers *[1 mark]* making it harder for them to slide over one another *[1 mark]*.
   c) e.g. corrosion-resistant *[1 mark]*
2 Aluminium *[1 mark]* because it has a low density/is light so the yacht would be able to move quickly in the water *[1 mark]* and aluminium doesn't corrode (unlike iron) so it would not be damaged over time by being in contact with water *[1 mark]*.

Answers

Page 53 — Acids and Alkalis

1 a) 0 to 14 *[1 mark]*
  b) neutral *[1 mark]*
  c) B *[1 mark]*

2

Indicator	Colour
Litmus paper	blue
Phenolphthalein	pink
Universal indicator	purple
Methyl orange	yellow

[3 marks for whole table correct, otherwise 1 mark for each correct answer.]

3 a) H^+ ions/hydrogen ions *[1 mark]*
  b) neutralisation *[1 mark]*
  c) $H^+_{(aq)} + OH^-_{(aq)} \rightarrow H_2O_{(l)}$
  [1 mark for the correct reactants and products, 1 mark for all state symbols correct.]

Page 54 — Reactions of Acids

1 a) magnesium sulfate + water *[1 mark]*
  b) aluminium chloride + hydrogen *[1 mark]*
2 a) nitric acid + copper oxide $\rightarrow$ copper nitrate + water *[1 mark]*
  b) $2HCl + Zn(OH)_2 \rightarrow ZnCl_2 + 2H_2O$ *[1 mark for the correct formulae, 1 mark for correct balancing.]*
  c) ammonium sulfate *[1 mark]*
3 a) carbon dioxide *[1 mark]*
Don't just give the formula of carbon dioxide — the question asks you to name the gas.
  b) $2HNO_3 + MgCO_3 \rightarrow Mg(NO_3)_2 + H_2O + CO_2$ *[1 mark for the correct formulae, 1 mark for correct balancing]*
  c) hydrochloric acid *[1 mark]*

Page 55 — Titrations

1 a) $0.1 \times (20 \div 1000) = $ **0.002 moles**
  [2 marks for correct answer, otherwise 1 mark for correct working.]
  b) ratio of moles of $HCl:Ca(OH)_2 = 2:1$
  $0.002 \div 2 = $ **0.001 moles** *[1 mark]*
  c) $0.001 \div (50 \div 1000) = $ **0.02 mol/dm³**
  [2 marks for correct answer, otherwise 1 mark for correct working.]
  d) Add an indicator to the $Ca(OH)_2$ solution *[1 mark]*. The end-point has been reached when the indicator changes colour *[1 mark]*.
2 a) Moles KOH = $0.10 \times (30.0 \div 1000) = 0.0030$
  Reaction equation shows that 2 moles of KOH react with 1 mole of H_2SO_4 so 0.0030 moles of KOH react with $0.0030 \div 2 = 0.0015$ moles of H_2SO_4
  Concentration = $0.0015 \div (10.0 \div 1000)$
  = **0.15 mol/dm³**
  [3 marks for correct answer, otherwise 1 mark for correct moles of KOH, 1 mark for correct moles of H_2SO_4.]
There are 0.0015 moles in 10 cm³ of H_2SO_4. So you need to calculate how many moles there are in 1 dm³ (1000 cm³) to get the concentration.
  b) M_r of H_2SO_4 is $(2 \times 1) + (1 \times 32) + (4 \times 16) = 98$
  Concentration = $0.15 \times 98 = $ **14.7 g/dm³**
  [2 marks for correct answer, otherwise 1 mark for correct working.]

Page 56 — Making Insoluble Salts

1 Silver chloride — insoluble *[1 mark]*
  Sodium nitrate — soluble *[1 mark]*
  Magnesium hydroxide — insoluble *[1 mark]*
2 a) E.g. lead nitrate/$Pb(NO_3)_2$ and magnesium sulfate/$MgSO_4$
  [1 mark for any soluble lead salt, 1 mark for any soluble sulfate salt.]
  b) The student has poured too much solution into the funnel / the level of the solution goes above the filter paper *[1 mark]*. This means that some of the solid could pass down the sides of the filter paper and into the conical flask below, reducing the amount of solid that's extracted from the solution *[1 mark]*.
  c) E.g. calcium chloride/$CaCl_2$ and sodium carbonate/Na_2CO_3
  [1 mark for any soluble calcium salt, 1 mark for any soluble carbonate.]

Page 57 — Making Soluble Salts

1 a) ammonium chloride *[1 mark]*
  b) No, because the salt will be contaminated by the indicator *[1 mark]*.
2 a) $H_2SO_{4(aq)} + CuO_{(s)} \rightarrow CuSO_{4(aq)} + H_2O_{(l)}$
  [1 mark for correct reactants and products, 1 mark for correct state symbols.]
  b) E.g. warm the sulfuric acid in a water bath *[1 mark]*. Add excess copper oxide to the acid *[1 mark]*. When the reaction is complete, filter the reaction mixture to remove the excess copper oxide *[1 mark]*. Heat the remaining solution gently (using a Bunsen burner) to evaporate off some of the water *[1 mark]*. Leave the solution to cool and allow the salt to crystallise *[1 mark]*. Filter off the solid salt and leave the crystals to dry *[1 mark]*.

Page 58 — Tests for Cations

1 a) E.g. take a clean platinum wire loop *[1 mark]*, dip it into the substance to be tested and put the material into the hot part of a Bunsen burner flame *[1 mark]*.
  b) Potassium would give a lilac flame *[1 mark]* but sodium would give a yellow-orange flame *[1 mark]*.
2 a) i) D *[1 mark]*
    ii) Ammonia gas turns damp red litmus paper blue *[1 mark]*.
  b) B *[1 mark]*
  c) $Fe^{2+}_{(aq)} + 2OH^-_{(aq)} \rightarrow Fe(OH)_{2(s)}$ *[1 mark]*

Page 59 — Tests for Anions

1 $Ba^{2+} + SO_4^{2-} \rightarrow BaSO_4$ *[1 mark]*
2 a) i) CO_3^{2-} *[1 mark]*
    ii) I^- *[1 mark]*
  b) i) dilute hydrochloric acid *[1 mark]*, barium chloride solution *[1 mark]*
    ii) a white precipitate *[1 mark]*
3 The presence of chloride ions could be tested by adding dilute nitric acid followed by silver nitrate solution *[1 mark]*. If chloride ions were present, a white precipitate would form *[1 mark]*.
  The presence of carbonate ions could be tested by adding dilute hydrochloric acid *[1 mark]*. If carbonate ions were present, bubbles of gas (carbon dioxide) will be released *[1 mark]*.

Page 60 — Tests for Gases and Water

1 a) Test the gas with a lighted splint *[1 mark]*. Hydrogen will burn with a squeaky pop *[1 mark]*.
  b) Test the gas with a glowing splint *[1 mark]*. Oxygen will relight it *[1 mark]*.

2 a) The powder would change colour from white *[1 mark]* to blue *[1 mark]*.

b) Pure water has a boiling point of 100 °C *[1 mark]* and a freezing point of 0 °C *[1 mark]*, so the liquid cannot be pure water *[1 mark]*.

c) Chlorine gas bleaches damp litmus paper *[1 mark]*. Carbon dioxide gas turns limewater cloudy *[1 mark]*. So the gas does contain carbon dioxide *[1 mark]* but it doesn't contain chlorine *[1 mark]*.

Section 5 — Physical Chemistry

Page 61 — Energy Transfer in Reactions

1 B *[1 mark]*

2 a) Endothermic *[1 mark]*. The temperature decrease shows that the reaction is taking in energy from the surroundings *[1 mark]*.

b) i) The overall change in energy during a reaction *[1 mark]*

ii) positive *[1 mark]*

iii) ΔH *[1 mark]*

3 E.g.

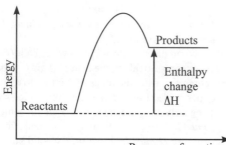

[1 mark for reactants and products correctly labelled and at appropriate energies, 1 mark for correct shape of curve, 1 mark for enthalpy change correctly labelled.]

Page 62 — Measuring Enthalpy Changes

1 a) To ensure that they are the same temperature before beginning the reaction / to know their initial temperature *[1 mark]*.

b) i) To insulate the cup *[1 mark]*.

ii) To reduce the energy lost by evaporation *[1 mark]*.

c) 31 °C – 21 °C = **10 °C** *[1 mark]*

d) The temperature of the reaction mixture *[1 mark]*.

e) The experiment could be repeated and an average temperature change calculated *[1 mark]*.

f) E.g. dissolving (or dissolution) / displacement *[1 mark]*.

Page 63 — Calculating Enthalpy Changes

1 a) Because copper conducts heat very well *[1 mark]*.

b) heat energy change (Q) = m × c × ΔT
= 50 × 4.2 × 30.5 = **6405 J** *[2 marks for correct answer, otherwise 1 mark for correct working.]*

c) Energy produced = 6405 ÷ 0.7
= 9150 J/g = **9.15 kJ/g** *[2 marks for correct answer, otherwise 1 mark for correct working.]*

2 a) M_r of ethanol = (2 × 12) + (6 × 1) + (1 × 16) = 46
Number of moles = 1.15 ÷ 46 = **0.025** *[2 marks for correct answer, otherwise 1 mark for correct working.]*

b) 7245 J = 7.245 kJ
Molar enthalpy change = −7.245 ÷ 0.025
= **−289.8 kJ/mol** *[2 marks for correct answer, otherwise 1 mark for correct working.]*

The molar enthalpy change (−289.8 kJ/mol) is negative because combustion is an exothermic reaction.

Page 64 — Bond Energies

1 (4 × 412) + (2 × 498) = 2644 kJ/mol *[1 mark]*
(2 × 743) + (4 × 463) = 3338 kJ/mol *[1 mark]*
Enthalpy change = 2644 − 3338 = **−694 kJ/mol**
[1 mark for correct value, 1 mark for correct sign]

2 a) 158 + (4 × 391) + 498 = 2220 kJ/mol *[1 mark]*
945 + (4 × 463) = 2797 kJ/mol *[1 mark]*
Enthalpy change = 2220 − 2797 = **−577 kJ/mol**
[1 mark for correct value, 1 mark for correct sign]

b) The reaction is exothermic *[1 mark]* as the energy change of reaction is negative / energy is given out during the reaction / it takes less energy to break the bonds in the reactants than the energy given out when the bonds in the products are made *[1 mark]*.

Pages 65-66 — Rates of Reaction

1 a) C *[1 mark]*.

b) activation energy *[1 mark]*

2 Produced most product: C *[1 mark]*, as the most mass was lost from the reaction vessel *[1 mark]*.
Finished first: B *[1 mark]*, as it is the first curve to flatten out *[1 mark]*.
Started at the slowest rate: A *[1 mark]*, as the gradient of the curve is the shallowest *[1 mark]*.

3 a) E.g.

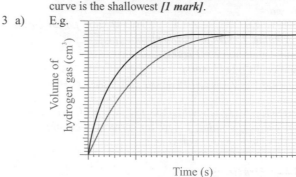

[1 mark for curve with steeper gradient at the start of the reaction, 1 mark for final volume being the same as for the other curve but reaching it in less time.]

b) The frequency of the collisions *[1 mark]* and the energy of the colliding particles *[1 mark]*.

c) There are more particles in a given volume/the particles are closer together *[1 mark]*, so the collisions between particles are more frequent *[1 mark]*.

d) The rate would increase *[1 mark]*.

e) Smaller pieces have a higher surface area to volume ratio *[1 mark]*. So for the same volume of solid, the particles around it will have more area to work on and collisions will be more frequent *[1 mark]*.

f) E.g. changing the temperature / adding a catalyst *[1 mark]*.

Page 67 — Catalysts

1 D *[1 mark]*

2 a) i) It's a catalyst *[1 mark]*.

ii) It provides an alternative reaction pathway *[1 mark]* with a lower activation energy *[1 mark]*.

b) The reaction equation won't change *[1 mark]*. Cerium oxide isn't used up in the reaction, so doesn't appear in the reaction equation *[1 mark]*.

c)

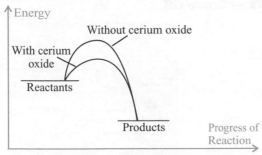

[1 mark for start and end energies being the same for reactions with and without cerium oxide, 1 mark for reaction with cerium oxide rising to a lower energy than reaction without cerium oxide]

Page 68 — Measuring Rates of Reaction

1   A *[1 mark]*
2 a) i)   E.g. the gas is released directly into the room and may be toxic/hazardous *[1 mark]*.
    ii)   E.g. measure the volume of gas given off using a gas syringe *[1 mark]*.
  b) i)   E.g. observe a marker through the solution *[1 mark]*. Measure how long it takes for the marker to disappear (as the precipitate forms) *[1 mark]*.
    ii)   The time taken for the mark to be obscured. / The rate of reaction. *[1 mark]*

Pages 69-70 — Rate of Reaction Experiments

1 a) $2H_2O_{2(aq)} \rightarrow 2H_2O_{(l)} + O_{2(g)}$
    [1 mark for correct formulae of products including their state symbols, 1 mark for correctly balancing the equation.]
  b) i)   17 cm^3 *[1 mark]*
    ii)   Manganese(IV) oxide was the most effective catalyst *[1 mark]* because it led to the greatest volume of oxygen being produced over the time period measured/increased the rate of reaction by the greatest amount *[1 mark]*.
2   B *[1 mark]*
3 a) i)   Draw a tangent to curve **Q** at 50 s, e.g.:

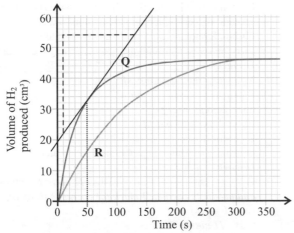

Then calculate the gradient of your tangent, e.g.:
Change in $y = 54 - 22 = 32$
Change in $x = 130 - 10 = 120$
Gradient = change in y ÷ change in x
        $= 32 \div 120 = $ **0.27 cm^3/s**
[Accept answers between 0.22 cm^3/s and 0.32 cm^3/s. 3 marks for correct answer, otherwise 1 mark for drawing a correct tangent and 1 mark for using the correct equation to calculate the gradient.]

It's OK if you've drawn your tangent slightly differently to this one, or if you've used a different bit of the tangent to calculate the gradient. As long as your tangent's sensible and your final answer is in the range given, you'll get the marks.
The same thing applies to the second tangent and calculation too...

    ii)   Draw a tangent to curve **R** at 120 s, e.g.:

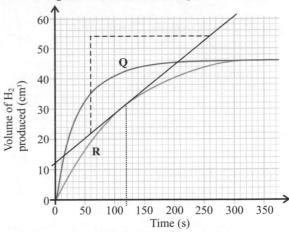

Then calculate the gradient of your tangent, e.g.:
Change in $y = 54 - 22 = 32$
Change in $x = 260 - 60 = 200$
Gradient = change in y ÷ change in x
        $= 32 \div 200 = $ **0.16 cm^3/s**
[Accept answers between 0.11 cm^3/s and 0.21 cm^3/s. 3 marks for correct answer, otherwise 1 mark for drawing a correct tangent and 1 mark for using the correct equation to calculate the gradient.]

  b)   Reaction Q must used powdered zinc. Powdered zinc has a larger surface area to volume ration than zinc ribbon *[1 mark]*, so the rate of reaction would be higher for powdered zinc than for zinc ribbon *[1 mark]*. The line for reaction Q has a steeper gradient / finishes sooner than the line for reaction R, so it must have a higher rate *[1 mark]*.
  c)   E.g. the student would have used the same volume / concentration of acid in each experiment *[1 mark]*. This variable needed to be controlled so that the student could tell that the variable he was changing was causing the results *[1 mark]*.

Pages 71-72 — Reversible Reactions

1 a)   It is reversible *[1 mark]*.
  b)   Both (the forward and reverse) reactions are taking place at exactly the same rate *[1 mark]*.
  c) i)   It takes in energy *[1 mark]*, because it's endothermic/all reversible reactions are exothermic in one direction and endothermic in the other direction. *[1 mark]*
    ii)   One reaction is exothermic and the other endothermic *[1 mark]*, so a change in temperature will favour one reaction more than the other *[1 mark]*.
    iii)   left *[1 mark]*
  d)   It won't affect the position of equilibrium *[1 mark]*, because there are the same number of moles of gas on either side of the equation *[1 mark]*.
Make sure you talk about the number of moles in your answer — if you only mention volume you won't get the mark.
  e)   It is not a closed system / the products can escape *[1 mark]*.
2 a)   Endothermic *[1 mark]*, because it is favoured by heating/heat is taken in *[1 mark]*.
  b) i)   It turns from white to blue *[1 mark]*.
    ii)   It increases *[1 mark]*.
3   The first student's reaction conditions are better *[1 mark]*, because:
The forward reaction is endothermic *[1 mark]* so raising the temperature will increase this reaction to use up the extra heat *[1 mark]*. There are more moles of gas on the right-hand side of the equation *[1 mark]*, and a lower pressure will encourage the reaction that produces more moles of gas *[1 mark]*.

Section 6 — Organic Chemistry

Pages 73-74 — Organic Compounds

1   B *[1 mark]*
2   A *[1 mark]*
3 a)   A group of compounds that can all be represented by the same general formula *[1 mark]*.
   b) i)

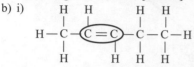

[1 mark]

     ii)   pent-2-ene *[1 mark]*
     iii) CH_2 *[1 mark]*
4

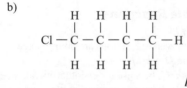

[1 mark]

5

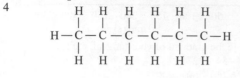

[1 mark]

6 a)   pentanoic acid *[1 mark]*
   b)   Yes it will, as compounds in the same homologous series react in similar ways *[1 mark]*.

Page 75 — Isomers

1   B *[1 mark]*
2 a)

[1 mark]

   b)

[1 mark]

[1 mark]

Don't worry if your answer doesn't look identical to what's shown here — as long as you drew an isomer with the Cl attached to one of the end carbons, and an isomer where it's attached to one of the middle carbons, you'd get the marks.

Page 76 — Crude Oil

1

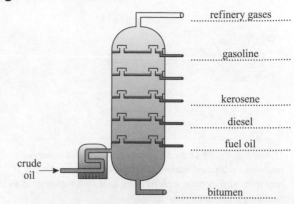

[3 marks for all 6 correct, 2 marks for at least 4 correct, 1 mark for at least 2 correct]

2 a)   E.g. fuel for large ships *[1 mark]* and in power stations *[1 mark]*.
   b)   Triacontane, e.g. because the fractionating column is hottest at the bottom *[1 mark]* so hydrocarbons with higher boiling points will be collected further down the column *[1 mark]*. Triacontane has a higher boiling point than heptane because triacontane is a bigger molecule *[1 mark]* (so triacontane will be collected lower down).

Page 77 — Cracking

1 a) $C_{10}H_{22} \rightarrow C_8H_{18} + C_2H_4$ *[1 mark]*
   b)   D *[1 mark]*
2 a) i)   It acts as a catalyst / catalyses the reaction *[1 mark]*.
     ii)   alkenes *[1 mark]*
   b)   There is a greater demand for short-chain alkanes than for longer-chain alkanes *[1 mark]*. To meet this demand, long hydrocarbons are split into more useful short-chain molecules *[1 mark]*. Cracking also produces alkenes *[1 mark]* which are used to make polymers/plastic *[1 mark]*.

Pages 78-79 — Burning Hydrocarbons

1   A *[1 mark]*
2 a)   Carbon monoxide can form if the fuel is burnt without enough oxygen / if incomplete combustion occurs *[1 mark]*.
   b)   Carbon monoxide can interfere with the blood's role of carrying oxygen around the body, meaning it can carry less *[1 mark]*.
3 a) i)   high temperatures *[1 mark]*
     ii)   E.g. in a car engine *[1 mark]*.
   b)   nitric acid *[1 mark]*
   c)   sulfur dioxide *[1 mark]*
4 a)   C *[1 mark]*
   b)   propane + oxygen → carbon dioxide + water *[1 mark]*
   c) i) $C_{12}H_{24} + 18O_2 \rightarrow 12CO_2 + 12H_2O$ *[1 mark for all reactants and products correct, 1 mark for correct balancing.]*
     ii)   soot *[1 mark]*
5 a) C_9H_{20} *[1 mark]*
   b)   e.g. sulfur *[1 mark]*

Page 80 — Alkanes

1   C *[1 mark]*
2 a) C_nH_{2n+2} *[1 mark]*
A general formula means you can replace the 'n's with a number to get the formula of a certain molecule in the series — so the 4th alkane is $C_4H_{(2\times4+2)} = C_4H_{10}$.
   b) i)   ethane *[1 mark]*
     ii)   6 *[1 mark]*

c)

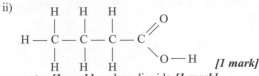

[1 mark]

d) i) methane + bromine $\xrightarrow{\text{UV}}$ bromomethane + hydrogen bromide
[1 mark for each correct product]

It doesn't matter which way round you write the two missing answers here.

  ii) substitution reaction [1 mark]

Page 81 — Alkenes

1 a) C_nH_{2n} [1 mark]

 b) A molecule that contains at least one (carbon-carbon) double bond / can make more bonds [1 mark].

2

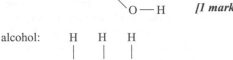

[1 mark]

You'd still get the mark if you drew the molecule with the Br atoms on the top instead of the bottom.

3 a) i) CH_2CHCH_3/CH_3CHCH_2 [1 mark]

  ii) The solution would turn from orange to colourless [1 mark].

  iii) An addition reaction [1 mark].

 b) Nothing would happen / the solution would stay orange [1 mark]. C_2H_6/ethane is a saturated hydrocarbon/an alkane/ doesn't contain a double bond [1 mark] so it can't react with bromine [1 mark].

Page 82 — Alcohols

1 a) propanol [1 mark]

 b) $CH_3CH_2OH/HOCH_2CH_3$ [1 mark]

 c)

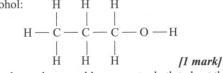

[1 mark]

2 a) Molecule Y must have reacted as it's an alcohol [1 mark]. When alcohols are added to potassium dichromate(VI), they are oxidised [1 mark] to form carboxylic acids [1 mark]. Molecule Z is an alkane, and so can't be oxidised by potassium dichromate(VI) [1 mark].

 b)

[1 mark]

Page 83 — Production of Ethanol

1 B [1 mark]

2 a)

Method	Reaction	Temperature needed
A	$C_2H_4 + \mathbf{H_2O} \rightarrow C_2H_5OH$	300 °C
B	$C_6H_{12}O_6 \rightarrow 2CO_2 + \mathbf{2}C_2H_5OH$	30 °C

[4 marks — 1 mark for each correct answer]

 b) Pressure — 60-70 atmospheres [1 mark]
Catalyst — phosphoric acid [1 mark]

 c) i) Any pH from 2-6 [1 mark]. The ethanol will react with oxygen in the air, converting it to ethanoic acid (which is acidic) [1 mark].

  ii) The enzyme in the yeast was denatured [1 mark] so it could not catalyse the reaction / the reaction could not happen [1 mark].

Page 84 — Carboxylic Acids

1 a) D [1 mark]

 b) HCOOH [1 mark]

 c) hydrogen/H_2 [1 mark]

2 a) i) butanoic acid [1 mark]

  ii)

[1 mark]

 b) water [1 mark], carbon dioxide [1 mark]

 c) ethanoic acid [1 mark]

Pages 85-86 — Esters

1 a) A volatile chemical evaporates easily [1 mark].

 b) They often smell nice/have distinctive smells [1 mark].

 c) e.g. as flavourings [1 mark]

2 a) e.g. sulfuric acid [1 mark]

It's usually sulfuric acid that's used as the catalyst for this reaction, but any named acid would be fine here.

 b) $CH_3COOH + \mathbf{CH_3CH_2OH} \rightarrow CH_3COOCH_2CH_3 + H_2O$
[1 mark]

 c) ethyl ethanoate [1 mark]

 d) -COO- [1 mark]

3 carboxylic acid:

[1 mark]

alcohol:

[1 mark]

4 a) E.g. the students could use a water bath to heat the reaction mixture. / The students could use a Bunsen burner to heat some water in a beaker and place a test tube containing the reaction mixture into the hot water. [1 mark]

You can have the mark here for any sensible method of heating the reaction mixture that doesn't involve holding it directly over an open flame.

 b) i) It is a catalyst / catalyses the reaction [1 mark].

  ii) E.g. wear gloves [1 mark] and safety goggles [1 mark].

 c)

[1 mark]

 d) E.g. smell the mixture. If it smells fruity/pleasant/sweet then an ester has been formed [1 mark].

 e) Carboxylic acid — propanoic acid [1 mark]
Alcohol — butanol [1 mark]

Pages 87-88 — Addition Polymers

1 a) B [1 mark]

 b) i) ethene [1 mark]

  ii) C=C [1 mark]

2 a) i)

[1 mark]

  ii)

[1 mark]

Don't worry if you put the CH₃ in another position — as long as it's attached to one of the carbon atoms, it's still correct.

iii) propene *[1 mark]*

b) poly(chloroethene) *[1 mark]*

c) E.g. most addition polymers are inert/don't react easily *[1 mark]*. This means that it takes a very long time for them to biodegrade and they can stay unchanged in landfill sites for a long time *[1 mark]*.

3

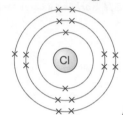

[1 mark]

4

F F
─(─C ─ C ─)─
F F   n

[1 mark]

Page 89 — Polyesters

1 D *[1 mark]*

2 a) i)

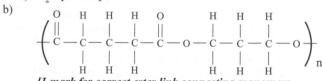

[1 mark for correct ester link connecting monomers, 1 mark for rest of the structure being correct.]

You could also draw the repeat unit with the monomers the other way round (so that the diol monomer is on the left-hand side and the dicarboxylic acid is on the right-hand side).

ii) H_2O *[1 mark]*

b)

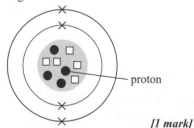

[1 mark for correct ester link connecting monomers, 1 mark for rest of the structure being correct.]

Practice Paper 1C

1 a) E.g.

[1 mark]

— proton

Remember that atoms have the same number of electrons and protons.

b) C and D *[1 mark]* — isotopes have the same number of protons but a different number of neutrons, and C and D are the only pair with the same number of protons *[1 mark]*.

c) Protons — 30 *[1 mark]*
Neutrons — 35 *[1 mark]*
Electrons — 30 *[1 mark]*

d) i) A compound is a substance made of two or more different elements *[1 mark]* that are chemically bonded together *[1 mark]*.

ii) $M_r = 65 + 32 + (4 \times 16) = \mathbf{161}$
[2 marks for the correct answer, otherwise 1 mark for correct working]

2 a) Nitrogen dioxide is created when the temperature is high enough for the nitrogen and oxygen in the air to react *[1 mark]*. This often happens in car engines, which there are lots of in cities *[1 mark]*.

b) i) nitric acid + calcium carbonate → calcium nitrate + carbon dioxide + water
[1 mark for calcium nitrate, 1 mark for carbon dioxide and water.]

Think back to acid and metal carbonate reactions — you always get a salt, carbon dioxide and water.

ii) e.g. sulfur dioxide *[1 mark]*

c) Nitrogen dioxide has a simple molecular structure *[1 mark]* and the molecules are held together by weak intermolecular forces *[1 mark]*. This means it has a very low boiling point, because not much energy is needed to break the molecules apart *[1 mark]*.

3 a) i) C *[1 mark]*

Melting point increases down the group, so chlorine will have a melting point about halfway between the melting points of fluorine and bromine.

ii) It is around halfway between the melting points of bromine and fluorine *[1 mark]*.

b) It is a red-brown *[1 mark]* liquid *[1 mark]*.

c) $Br_2 + 2KI \rightarrow I_2 + 2KBr$
[1 mark for correct reactants and products, 1 mark for correct balancing]

d) i)

[1 mark]

ii) The group number is equal to the number of electrons in the outer electron shell *[1 mark]*. Chlorine is in Group 7, so a chlorine atom has seven electrons in its outer shell *[1 mark]*.

e) Chlorine will displace the iodine in solution to form sodium chloride solution *[1 mark]*. This happens because chlorine is higher up Group 7 than iodine *[1 mark]*, which means that chlorine is more reactive *[1 mark]*.

f) When hydrogen chloride is dissolved in water, the hydrogen chloride molecules split up into H^+ ions and Cl^- ions *[1 mark]*. It is the H^+ ions that make the solution acidic *[1 mark]*.

4 a) Any two from: Problem — the spots of dye/ink are touching the solvent *[1 mark]*. Correction — the student should put the filter paper in a beaker of solvent with the pencil line above the level of the solvent *[1 mark]*. / Problem — the ink and dyes are compared using different solvents *[1 mark]*. Correction — the student should use the same solvent for the black ink and the dyes so that it's a fair test *[1 mark]*. / Problem — the ink and dyes are compared on different pieces of filter paper which could make it difficult to directly compare them *[1 mark]*. Correction — the student should put the spots of the dyes and the ink on the same piece of filter paper *[1 mark]*.

b) Dyes B and D *[1 mark]*
Explanation — the spots from these two dyes are in the same positions as the spots from the black ink *[1 mark]*.

c) R_f = distance travelled by solute ÷ distance travelled by solvent = 4.8 ÷ 6.4 = **0.75** *[1 mark]*

5 a)   magnesium oxide *[1 mark]*
  b)

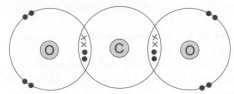

  [1 mark for all shared pairs correct, 1 mark for the non-bonding electrons correct]

  c) $M_r(MgCO_3) = 24 + 12 + (16 \times 3) = 84$
    percentage mass of C $= (12 \div 84) \times 100 =$ **14%**
    [2 marks for correct answer, otherwise 1 mark for correct working.]

  d) i)   Greenhouse gases act like an insulating layer by absorbing heat that would normally be radiated from the Earth into space *[1 mark]* and re-radiating some of it back towards the Earth *[1 mark]*.
    ii)   0.04% *[1 mark]*
    iii)   e.g. global warming / climate change / changing rainfall patterns / sea level rise *[1 mark]*

6 a) i)   Add sodium hydroxide (NaOH) solution *[1 mark]*. Iron(II) chloride will form a green precipitate. Iron(III) chloride will form a reddish-brown precipitate *[1 mark]*.
    ii)   Add dilute nitric acid (HNO_3) followed by silver nitrate ($AgNO_3$) solution *[1 mark]*. Sodium chloride will form a white precipitate. Sodium iodide will form a yellow precipitate *[1 mark]*.
  b)   sodium carbonate / sodium hydrogen carbonate *[1 mark for identifying the sodium ion and 1 mark for identifying the carbonate ion.]*

7 a)   The volume of gas produced *[1 mark]*.
  b)   hydrogen/H_2 *[1 mark]*
  c)   Reaction D *[1 mark]*. The most reactive metal will react fastest with the acid *[1 mark]*. In reaction D the largest volume of gas has been collected in the syringe / the most bubbles are being given off *[1 mark]*.
  d)   e.g. zinc *[1 mark]*
You would get this mark if you named any metal between magnesium and iron in the reactivity series (for example, aluminium would be fine here too).
  e)   Reaction of copper sulfate with iron: yes *[1 mark]*
    Reaction of iron sulfate with magnesium: yes *[1 mark]*
  f)   Mg / magnesium *[1 mark]*
Remember, when you're talking about oxidation and reduction in terms of electrons, oxidation is the loss of electrons. In this reaction, the magnesium went from being neutral atoms to positively charged ions — so they must have lost electrons.

8 a)   propene *[1 mark]*
  b)   alkenes *[1 mark]*
  c)
```
    H   H   H   H   H
    |   |   |   |   |
H — C — C — C — C — C — H
    |   |   |   |   |
    H   H   H   H   H       [1 mark]
```
  d)   Test: Add a few drops of bromine water to the gas and shake *[1 mark]*.
    Observations: Gas A (propane) will have no effect. Gas B (propene) will change the bromine water from orange to colourless *[1 mark]*.
  e)   The C=C double bond is split *[1 mark]* and a bromine atom is added to each carbon atom *[1 mark]*.
  f) $C_3H_8 + 5O_2 \rightarrow 3CO_2 + 4H_2O$
    [1 mark for products and reactants, 1 mark for balancing]
  g) i)   cracking *[1 mark]*
    ii)   Gas B/propene, heptane, decane *[1 mark]*.

9 a)   A reaction that gives out energy to the surroundings (usually in the form of heat) *[1 mark]*.
  b)   E.g. measure the temperature of some water, add the substance and stir, then measure the temperature every 30 seconds and record the lowest temperature reached *[1 mark]*. Repeat the experiment with other substances to determine which is the most effective *[1 mark]*. The same volume of water and mass/volume of substance should be used for each experiment *[1 mark]*.
  c) $Fe_2O_3 + 3Ca \rightarrow 3CaO + 2Fe$
    [1 mark for the correct reactants and products, 1 mark for correct balancing]

10 a)   E.g.

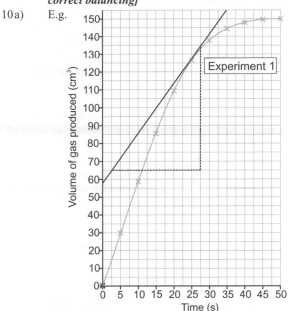

  rate of reaction = change in y ÷ change in x
  $= (135 - 65) \div (27.5 - 2.5)$
  $= 70 \div 25 =$ **2.8 cm³/s**
  (accept answers between 2 and 3 cm³/s)
  [3 marks for correct answer, otherwise 1 mark for correctly drawn tangent, 1 mark for dividing change in y by change in x.]

  b)

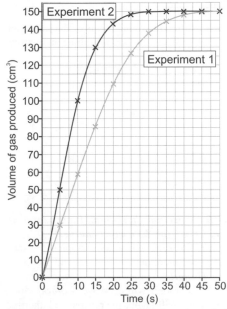

  [1 mark for correctly plotted points, 1 mark for curve of best fit]
  c)   7-8 seconds (to collect 75 cm³) *[1 mark]*
The total volume is 150 cm³, so you need to read off the value from 75 cm³ on your graph.
  d)   The rate of reaction decreases as the reaction proceeds *[1 mark]*.

e) It increases the rate of the reaction. The graph for experiment 2 has a steeper slope at the beginning. / The reaction is complete in less time *[1 mark]*.

f) Catalysts make reactions happen faster by providing an alternative reaction pathway with a lower activation energy *[1 mark]*.

11 a) Oxygen *[1 mark]* and water *[1 mark]* must be present.

b) C *[1 mark]*

c) i) sacrificial protection *[1 mark]*

ii) Magnesium is more reactive than iron *[1 mark]*, so the magnesium will be oxidised instead of the iron *[1 mark]*.

d) galvanising *[1 mark]*

12 a) $M_r(Mg) = 24$
$M_r(MgCl_2) = 24 + (35.5 \times 2) = 95$
moles of $MgCl_2$ = mass ÷ M_r = 7.60 ÷ 95 = 0.08 moles
From the equation, 1 mole of $MgCl_2$ is produced from 1 mole of Mg. So 0.08 moles of $MgCl_2$ will be produced from 0.08 moles of Mg.
So mass of Mg = 0.08 × 24 = 1.92 g
[3 marks for correct answer, otherwise 1 mark for correctly calculating the M_rs, 1 mark for correct number of moles of $MgCl_2$ and Mg.]

b) Test: test the gas with a lighted splint *[1 mark]*.
Observation: hydrogen produces a squeaky pop *[1 mark]*.

c) E.g. the hydrochloric acid/HCl was used in excess *[1 mark]*.

13 a) Mass of Cu: 33.08 − 28.00 = 5.08
Mass of O: 34.36 − 33.08 = 1.28
Number of moles: Cu = 5.08 ÷ 63.5 = 0.08
              O = 1.28 ÷ 16 = 0.08
Simplest whole number ratio:
(0.08 ÷ 0.08) : (0.08 ÷ 0.08) = 1 : 1
Empirical formula: CuO
[5 marks for correct answer, otherwise 1 mark for calculating the mass of Cu, 1 mark for calculating the mass of O, 1 mark for correct number of moles of each element, 1 mark for finding the simplest whole number ratio.]

b) i) percentage yield = (1.20 ÷ 1.80) × 100 = **66.7%** *[2 marks for correct answer, otherwise 1 mark for correct working.]*

ii) E.g. not all of the metal may have reacted *[1 mark]*.

Practice Paper 2C

1 a) i) Isotopes are different atomic forms of the same element, which have the same number of protons but a different number of neutrons *[1 mark]*.

ii) Cl is 25% ^{37}Cl and 75% ^{35}Cl *[1 mark]*
$A_r = (37 \times 25 ÷ 100) + (35 \times 75 ÷ 100) = 35.5$ *[1 mark]*

b) E.g.

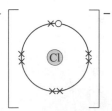

[1 mark for 8 electrons in sodium, 1 mark for 8 electrons in chlorine, 1 mark for the correct charges]

2 a) The forward and reverse reactions happen at exactly the same rate. / The concentrations of reactants and products remain the same. *[1 mark]*

b) The yield of ammonia will decrease *[1 mark]*. Increasing the temperature will favour the reverse/endothermic reaction which takes in energy *[1 mark]*.

c) The yield of ammonia will decrease *[1 mark]*. This is because lowering the pressure will encourage the reaction that produces more moles of gas (there are four moles of gas on the left-hand side of the equation, for every two moles on the right) *[1 mark]*.

d) i) M_r of ammonia = 14 + (3 × 1) = 17
Number of moles of ammonia = mass ÷ M_r
= 85 ÷ 17 = **5 moles**
[2 marks for correct answer, otherwise 1 mark for correct working.]

ii) Volume = moles × 24 = **120 dm³** *[1 mark]*

The molar volume of a gas is 24 dm³, so you need to multiply that value by the number of moles.

3 a) propanol/propan-1-ol *[1 mark]*

b) i) propanoic acid *[1 mark]*

ii) ester *[1 mark]*

iii) E.g. it is volatile *[1 mark]*.

c) i) $C_2H_5OH + 3O_2 \rightarrow 3H_2O + 2CO_2$
[1 mark for the correct reactants and products, 1 mark for correctly balancing the equation.]

ii) E.g. microbial oxidation / heating with potassium dichromate(VI) in dilute sulfuric acid *[1 mark]*

4 a) Any two from: e.g. fizzing increases from lithium to potassium / sodium and potassium melt, but lithium doesn't / a flame is only seen with potassium *[2 marks — 1 mark for each correct answer]*.

b) E.g. Group 1 elements further down the group have an outer electron in a shell that is further from the nucleus *[1 mark]*. So as you go down the group, the attraction between the outer shell electron and the nucleus becomes less and so the electron is more easily lost *[1 mark]*.

c) $2Li + 2H_2O \rightarrow 2LiOH + H_2$
[1 mark for the correct reactants and products, 1 mark for correctly balancing the equation.]

d) The student could put the wire loop in one of the unlabelled samples and then hold it in a blue Bunsen flame *[1 mark]*. If the flame turns crimson-red, the sample is lithium chloride, but if it turns lilac, the sample is potassium chloride *[1 mark]*.

5 a) Bonds broken (2 × 436) + 498 = 1370 *[1 mark]*
Bonds formed (4 × 464) = 1856 *[1 mark]*
Enthalpy change = 1370 − 1856 = **−486 kJ/mol**
[1 mark for the correct value, 1 mark for the correct sign]

b) endothermic *[1 mark]*

c) D *[1 mark]*

6 a)

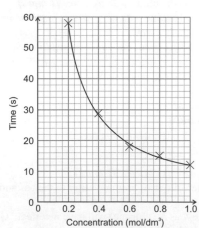

[1 mark for plotting points correctly, 1 mark for sensible curve of best fit.]

b) E.g. 23 s (accept 22-24 s) *[1 mark]*

c) Repeat the experiment and take the mean of the results *[1 mark]*

d) The rate increases as the concentration increases *[1 mark]*.

e) At higher concentration there are more particles in a certain space / the particles are closer together *[1 mark]*. This means that collisions between particles happen more often / there are more frequent collisions / there are more collisions per second *[1 mark]*.

    f)   No. The magnesium has a larger surface area
            [1 mark]. This will increase the rate of the reaction
            [1 mark], so it will take less than 18 seconds
            for 20 cm^3 of hydrogen to form *[1 mark]*.

7 a)   E.g. methyl orange / phenolphthalein *[1 mark]*

   b) $H_2SO_{4(aq)} + Ca(OH)_{2(aq)} \rightarrow CaSO_{4(aq)} + 2H_2O_{(l)}$
            [1 mark for the correct formula for calcium sulfate,
            1 mark for correctly balancing the equation]

   c) i) $(8.80 \div 1000) \times 0.050 =$ **0.00044 moles** *[1 mark]*

     ii) 0.00044 moles *[1 mark]*

From the equation you can see that one mole of H_2SO_4 reacts with one mole of $Ca(OH)_2$ so the number of moles of each will be the same.

    iii) 10 cm^3 ÷ 1000 = 0.01 dm^3
          concentration = moles ÷ volume
          0.00044 ÷ 0.01 = **0.044 mol/dm^3** *[1 mark]*

8 a)   So the ions are free to move *[1 mark]* so they can
            carry the current / conduct electricity *[1 mark]*.

   b) $2Cl^- \rightarrow Cl_2 + 2e^-$ *[1 mark]*

   c)   The sodium ions are more reactive than the hydrogen
            ions, so hydrogen gas will be formed *[1 mark]*.

   d)   sodium hydroxide *[1 mark]*

   e)   Aluminium is more reactive than carbon (so the carbon
            will not be able to reduce the aluminium oxide) *[1 mark]*.

   f)   Aluminium has a low density, which
            makes it relatively light *[1 mark]*.

   g) $M_r(Al_2O_3) = (2 \times 27) + (3 \times 16) = 102$
            moles = mass ÷ M_r
            moles of $Al_2O_3 = 40.8 \div 102 = 0.400$ moles
            From the balanced equation, 2 moles of aluminium oxide
            produce 4 moles of aluminium.
            So, 0.400 moles of aluminium oxide will produce
            $(0.400 \div 2) \times 4 = 0.800$ moles of aluminium.
            $A_r(Al) = 27$, so mass of Al $= 0.800 \times 27 = 21.6$ g
            [4 marks for correct answer, otherwise 1 mark for
            correctly calculating M_r of Al_2O_3, 1 mark for correctly
            calculating the number of moles of Al_2O_3 and 1 mark
            for working out how many moles of Al are made.]

9 a) i) The solid stops dissolving and remains at
            the bottom of the flask *[1 mark]*.

    ii) zinc chloride *[1 mark]* and water *[1 mark]*.

   b)   E.g. do a titration to find out how much acid and
            alkali are needed for neutralisation *[1 mark]*. Add
            these volumes of acid and alkali together without
            indicator *[1 mark]*. Heat the solution to evaporate the
            water, leaving a dry sample of the salt *[1 mark]*.

   c)   B *[1 mark]* and E *[1 mark]*

For this reaction you need to pick two soluble salts — one that contains Ba^{2+} and one that contains SO_4^{2-}.

Working Out Your Grade

- Do both exam papers.

- Use the answers and mark scheme to mark each exam paper.

- Use the tables below to record your marks.

Paper 1

Q	Mark	Q	Mark
1		8	
2		9	
3		10	
4		11	
5		12	
6		13	
7			
Total			/110

Paper 2

Q	Mark	Q	Mark
1		6	
2		7	
3		8	
4		9	
5			
Total			/70

- Add together your marks for the two papers to give a total mark out of 180.

Total Mark = Paper 1 Total + Paper 2 Total

Total Mark = ☐ /180

- Look up your total mark in this table to see what grade you got.

Total Mark	Grade
160	9
139	8
118	7
106	6
94	5
82	4
67	3
53	2
38	1
0	U

Important!

The grade boundaries above are given as a guide only.
Exam boards tinker with their boundaries each year, so any grade you get on these practice papers is no guarantee of getting that grade in the real exam — but it should give you a pretty good idea.

CEQI42